Property of Stan Klein

ATLAS OF
HUMAN HISTOLOGY

MARIANO S. H. DI FIORE

*Associate Professor of Histology and Embryology, Faculty of Medical Sciences, University
of Buenos Aires and Head of the Laboratory of the Juan A. Fernández Hospital*

THIRD EDITION

III ORIGINAL COLOR PLATES
189 FIGURES

LEA & FEBIGER
PHILADELPHIA

ATLAS DE HISTOLOGIA NORMAL

Libreria "El Ateneo" Editorial

BUENOS AIRES-ARGENTINA

First Edition, 1957
Second Edition, 1963
Third Edition, 1967

Reprinted January, 1968, May, 1969

SBN 8121–0064–6

Library of Congress Catalog Card Number: 67–13890
Printed in the United States of America

FOREWORD TO THE THIRD EDITION

The medical student is frequently left on his own to pursue his studies. In some schools the instructor purposely employs such a procedure to develop initiative and self-reliance in the student. In other schools the marked growth in medical education has produced a shortage of personnel to meet instructional needs in the basic medical sciences. It is with these thoughts in mind that Dr. di Fiore's ATLAS OF HUMAN HISTOLOGY is presented by the publisher as a right hand to the student receiving initial instruction in histology and to the instructor as an aid in conserving his time.

The illustrations are designed as composite drawings of what may be seen by the student only after a study of several slides. This is done for the pure didactic purpose of reducing the number of illustrations necessary for study, and to curtail the cost of publication. The illustrations are designed to cover the *principles of histology* clearly and concisely. They are not intended to present the student with a bewildering array of every last item known to the professional histologist.

It is felt that Dr. di Fiore's ATLAS offers an admirable reference work for the student, with a minimum of words and a maximum of clarity. It is not intended to supplant a textbook of histology but rather to stand as a supplementary book.

The earlier editions of Dr. di Fiore's ATLAS met with unusual success. From the many students and faculty members who use the book have come excellent suggestions. This third edition has been revised by Dr. Ida G. Schmidt of the University of California at Davis. She has utilized many of the suggestions in rewriting much of the text and in improving the illustrations. Under her direction the ATLAS has been enhanced by 10 full new plates and numerous changes and additions to many of the plates previously used. This third edition, therefore, should be even more useful to its audience than heretofore.

THE PUBLISHER

CONTENTS

INDEX OF PLATES

ABBREVIATIONS ON PLATES

h. s. — horizontal section
l. s. — longitudinal section
o. s. — oblique section
tg. s. — tangential section
t. s. — transverse section
v. s. — vertical section

PLATE 1

OÖCYTE IN A DEVELOPING FOLLICLE

The large cell in the center of the plate, the oöcyte or female germ cell (2), shows features common to all cells, as they are seen in a routinely prepared section. The oöcyte is limited by the cell membrane or oölemma (1). The cytoplasm is granular and shows clear areas alternating irregularly with areas stained more or less intensely pink. The nucleus (3) is spherical and placed eccentrically; it is surrounded by the nuclear membrane (8) and contains nucleoplasm, clumps of chromatin, and the spherical, acidophilic nucleolus (9). (Nucleoli in most other types of cells are usually basophilic.)

The prominent pink band surrounding the oöcyte is the zone pellucida (7a), a special feature of this cell; it is a clear area in the living tissue. Radiating from the zona pellucida are several layers of epithelial cells. As in many other cell types, cell membranes are not clearly defined; the shape of the cell is indicated by that of the nucleus. Nearest the oöcyte is the corona radiata, a layer of columnar cells (4). Follicular cells, which are cuboid or polyhedral (7), make up the remaining layers. Surrounding these are spindle-shaped connective tissue cells with elongated nuclei, composing the follicular theca (6).

A cell in the process of mitosis is shown (10); its chromosomes are in the equatorial plate (metaphase). A blood capillary (11) is seen between the cells of the inner theca. Small spaces containing follicular fluid (5) are present among the cells of the follicular epithelium.

PLATE 1

OÖCYTE IN A DEVELOPING OVARIAN FOLLICLE

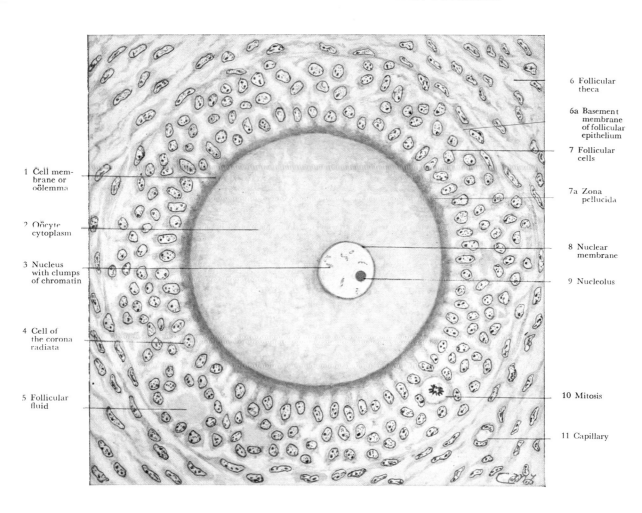

1 Cell membrane or oölemma

2 Oöcyte cytoplasm

3 Nucleus with clumps of chromatin

4 Cell of the corona radiata

5 Follicular fluid

6 Follicular theca

6a Basement membrane of follicular epithelium

7 Follicular cells

7a Zona pellucida

8 Nuclear membrane

9 Nucleolus

10 Mitosis

11 Capillary

Stain: hematoxylin-eosin. 650×.

PLATE 2 (Fig. 1)

DISSOCIATED SQUAMOUS EPITHELIAL CELLS

The field drawn corresponds to a "fresh" preparation of epithelial cells obtained by scraping the mucosa lining the mouth. The cells are seen isolated (1, 3) or in strips (2); in the strips the cells are closely knit together to make up epithelial tissue.

The cells have the shape of irregular polygons, and their cytoplasm is granular. The nucleus, centrally placed, is a small homogeneous refringent oval (5). Some of the cells are seen in side-view (4), and their thinness can be observed; they are squamous or pavement epithelial cells.

PLATE 2 (Fig. 2)

MESOTHELIUM OF THE PERITONEUM (SURFACE VIEW)

A piece of rabbit mesentery treated with silver nitrate solution and exposed to light has been dehydrated and mounted in balsam. Intercellular substance shows up black or dark brown (1) where silver nitrate has been reduced (intercellular cement). The cytoplasm of the mesothelial cells which form this tissue appears light brown. The nuclei are not stained; they occupy the clear space, usually eccentrically placed, seen in each of the cells (2). Some of the intercellular lines show thickenings which have been interpreted as stomata, but are probably artifacts.

PLATE 2 (Fig. 3)

SIMPLE SQUAMOUS EPITHELIUM: MESOTHELIUM OF THE PERITONEUM (TRANSVERSE SECTION)

In this figure is illustrated a simple squamous epithelium, mesothelium, seen in transverse section as it covers the wall of the jejunum. The cells are spindle-shaped with prominent, oval nuclei (1). Cell boundaries are not seen distinctly but are indicated in the depressed areas (2) where the cells taper and join each other. A fine basement membrane is recognizable in places (3). In surface view, these cells look like those in Fig. 2 above.

Mesothelium and the layer of underlying loose connective tissue (4) form the serosa (peritoneum), the outermost layer of the wall of the jejunum; this is attached to the muscularis externa (6). In the connective tissue layer may be seen small blood vessels, which are lined by a simple squamous endothelium (5).

— 16 —

PLATE 2

EPITHELIAL TISSUE

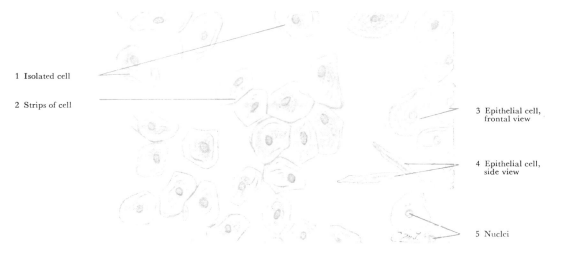

1 Isolated cell

2 Strips of cell

3 Epithelial cell,
frontal view

4 Epithelial cell,
side view

5 Nuclei

FIG. 1. — *Dissociated squamous epithelial cells.*

Observed in the fresh state. 110×.

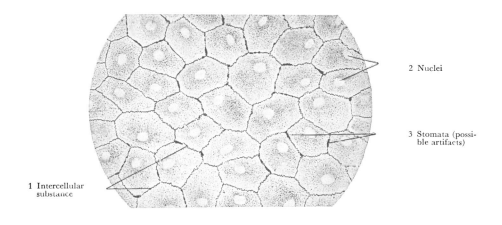

2 Nuclei

3 Stomata (possi-
ble artifacts)

1 Intercellular
substance

FIG. 2. — *Mesothelium of the peritoneum.*

Stain: silver nitrate. 230×.

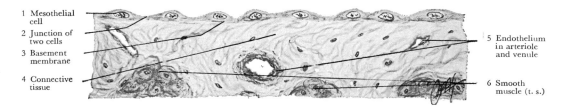

1 Mesothelial
cell

2 Junction of
two cells

3 Basement
membrane

4 Connective
tissue

5 Endothelium
in arteriole
and venule

6 Smooth
muscle (t. s.)

FIG. 3. — *Simple squamous epithelium (transverse section).*

Stain: hematoxylin-eosin. 500×.

PLATE 3 (Fig. 1)

SIMPLE COLUMNAR EPITHELIAL TISSUE

A cross section of gastric mucosa is illustrated.

Columnar epithelial cells (2, 5) are shown in linear arrangement as indicated by their nuclei (8). The ovoid nuclei, lengthened like the cells, are in the basal region of the latter.

A large quantity of cytoplasm, stained light pink in these mucous cells, can be seen above the nucleus in each cell. There is no appreciable differentiation at the apex of the cell.

In certain parts, the epithelium has been cut transversally, *i.e.*, parallel to its surface. Where this occurs close to the surface, the cells are seen end on, through their apices, and have the appearance of forming a mosaic of enucleated cells (1) showing their polygonal contour. Where the section cuts the basal end of the cells, the nuclei are cut transversally, resembling stratified epithelium (7).

Below the epithelium is the lamina propria (4, 9, 10), composed of connective tissue. A thin basement membrane (3), scarcely visible in these preparations, separates the epithelium from the lamina propria. Blood vessels (6) are present in the lamina propria.

The light appearance of the cytoplasm in this columnar epithelium is due to solution of mucinogen droplets during preparation of the tissues. In other simple columnar epithelial cells, where mucinogen is not a prominent component, the cytoplasm appears granular and stains more deeply. Examples of this may be seen in bile ducts of the liver (Plate 72, Fig. 1) and in interlobular ducts of the pancreas (Plate 75, Fig. 1:3, 19).

PLATE 3 (Fig. 2)

SIMPLE COLUMNAR EPITHELIUM WITH STRIATED BORDER

Free ends of intestinal villi are illustrated, showing columnar epithelium (2, 14), with a striated border on the apex of the cells (13), which is seen as a bright red line. Goblet cells (8, 12) are also shown; the goblet is stained lightly or not at all; the nucleus and cytoplasm are displaced to the base of the cell.

Between the cells of the epithelium may be found a few lymphocytes (6), which can be recognized by the deeply stained small, round nucleus.

The epithelium of the tip of a villus (lower center of the figure) has been sectioned obliquely, and has the typical appearance of a mosaic of enucleated cells (7).

A basement membrane (5), slightly more visible than in the previous figure, separates the epithelium from the lamina propria. A lymphatic vessel (3), capillaries (9) and smooth muscle as isolated fibers or in small groups (4, 11), are present in the lamina propria.

— 18 —

PLATE 3

EPITHELIAL TISSUE

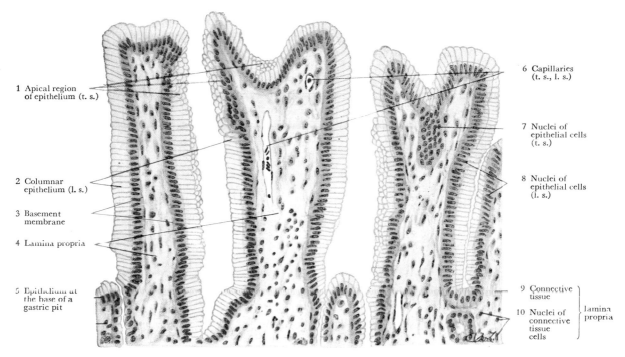

1 Apical region
of epithelium (t. s.)

2 Columnar
epithelium (l. s.)

3 Basement
membrane

4 Lamina propria

5 Epithelium at
the base of a
gastric pit

6 Capillaries
(t. s., l. s.)

7 Nuclei of
epithelial cells
(t. s.)

8 Nuclei of
epithelial cells
(l. s.)

9 Connective
tissue
} lamina
propria
10 Nuclei of
connective
tissue
cells

FIG. 1. — *Simple columnar epithelial tissue.*
Stain: hematoxylin-eosin. 250×.

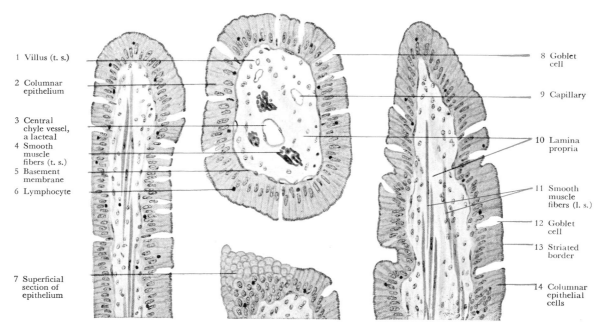

1 Villus (t. s.)

2 Columnar
epithelium

3 Central
chyle vessel,
a lacteal
4 Smooth
muscle
fibers (t. s.)
5 Basement
membrane
6 Lymphocyte

7 Superficial
section of
epithelium

8 Goblet
cell

9 Capillary

10 Lamina
propria

11 Smooth
muscle
fibers (l. s.)
12 Goblet
cell
13 Striated
border

14 Columnar
epithelial
cells

FIG. 2. — *Simple columnar epithelial tissue.*
Stain: hematoxylin-eosin. 250×.

PLATE 4 (Fig.1)

STRATIFIED SQUAMOUS EPITHELIUM
(TRANSVERSE SECTION)

The epithelium illustrated (1) lines the esophagus. It is made of numerous superimposed cell layers. The deep cells (5) are columnar and contain little cytoplasm. Their ovoid nuclei contain much chromatin. Mitosis (7) is occasionally in evidence.

Cells of the middle layers are polyhedral (4) with rounded or somewhat flattened nuclei.

The outer layers have flat, pavement-like cells, with a lenticular nucleus, disposed parallel to the surface of the epithelium (3).

Cell limits are visible in the middle and outer layers. They appear as thin pink lines, somewhat darker than the cytoplasm, and can best be observed with reduced light.

A basement membrane, hardly visible, separates the epithelium (1) from the underlying lamina propria (2). The esophagus has a papillary lamina propria, therefore the implantation of the epithelium follows a wavy line. The papillae (10) are cones of connective tissue, which seem to penetrate into the epithelium, but in reality the basal layer of the epithelium covers the papillae, and is lifted by them.

PLATE 4 (Fig. 2)

STRATIFIED SQUAMOUS EPITHELIUM
(TANGENTIAL SECTION)

A section has been made parallel to the surface of the epithelium, at the level of the line a-a of Figure 1.

Polyhedral cells (7) of the middle layers are seen; also basal cells (6) surrounding the papillae (1, 5, 8) of the lamina propria which are here seen sectioned transversally.

This is a typical section illustrating the different structures which make up the papillae: capillaries (2, 4) surrounded by connective tissue containing fibroblasts (3). Also shown is the relation between the papillae and the basal cells of the epithelium.

PLATE 4

EPITHELIAL TISSUE

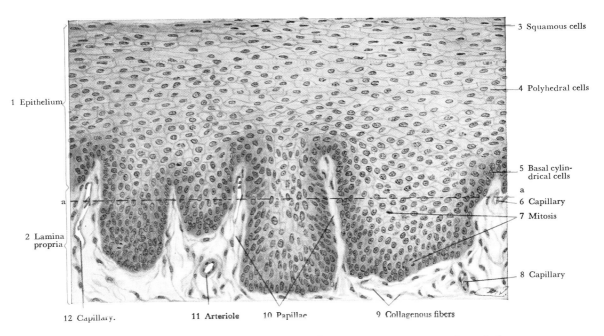

1 Epithelium

3 Squamous cells

4 Polyhedral cells

5 Basal cylin-
drical cells

a

6 Capillary

7 Mitosis

a

2 Lamina
propria

8 Capillary

12 Capillary.   11 Arteriole   10 Papillae   9 Collagenous fibers

FIG. 1. — *Stratified squamous epithelium, taken from a transverse section of the
esophagus.*
Stain: hematoxylin-eosin. 215×.

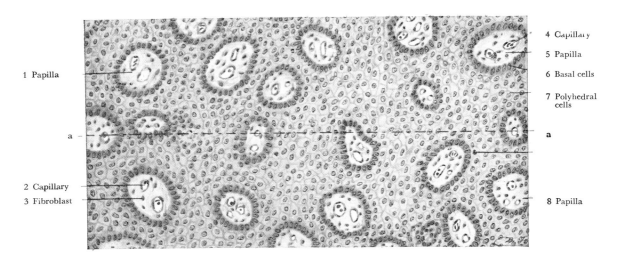

1 Papilla

4 Capillary

5 Papilla

6 Basal cells

7 Polyhedral
cells

a

a

2 Capillary
3 Fibroblast

8 Papilla

FIG. 2. — *Stratified squamous epithelium, a tangential section of the esophagus.*
Stain: hematoxylin-eosin. 215×.

PLATE 5 (Fig. 1)

PSEUDOSTRATIFIED COLUMNAR CILIATED EPITHELIUM

In this type of epithelium the cells appear to be distributed in several layers because their nuclei are situated at different levels. Careful observation of serial sections shows that all the cells are in contact with the basement membrane. The epithelium is not stratified but pseudostratified.

The deeply placed nuclei are those belonging to round cells (6), those of the middle parts to columnar cells (4), which have cilia (3), or to goblet mucous cells (5). A few pachychromatic spherical nuclei belong to migrating lymphocytes (8).

The basement membrane (7) is clearly seen separating the surface epithelium (1) from the underlying lamina propia (2). In this type of epithelium, the basement membrane is thick and prominent, in contrast to the very thin membrane seen in other epithelia.

PLATE 5 (Fig. 2)

TRANSITIONAL EPITHELIUM

Epithelium of the urinary bladder is composed of several layers of similar cells with rounded nuclei. This similarity of the cells differentiates this type of epithelium from stratified squamous epithelium, in which the cells of the various layers have different shapes.

In transitional epithelium, the cell shapes vary somewhat according to whether the mucosa is contracted or distended. When contracted, the cells are generally rounded or may tend to be somewhat cuboid or columnar. When distended (as in this illustration), the number of cell layers is reduced. The cells of the outer layers are more elongated or somewhat flattened, but not so much so that they appear squamous.

PLATE 5

EPITHELIAL TISSUE

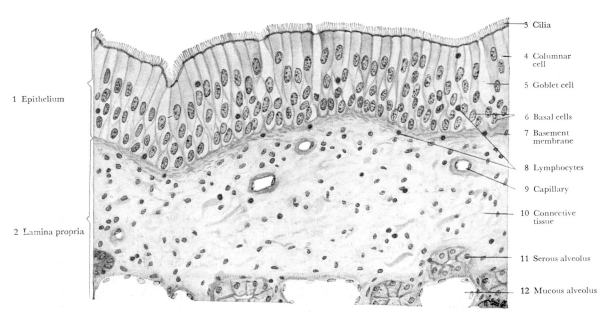

1 Epithelium

2 Lamina propria

3 Cilia

4 Columnar cell

5 Goblet cell

6 Basal cells

7 Basement membrane

8 Lymphocytes

9 Capillary

10 Connective tissue

11 Serous alveolus

12 Mucous alveolus

Fig. 1. — *Pseudostratified columnar ciliated epithelium.*
Stain: hematoxylin-eosin. 330×.

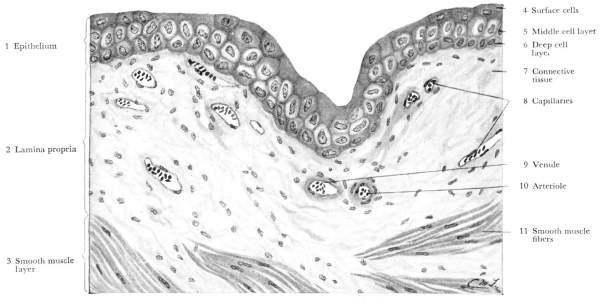

1 Epithelium

2 Lamina propria

3 Smooth muscle layer

4 Surface cells

5 Middle cell layer

6 Deep cell layer

7 Connective tissue

8 Capillaries

9 Venule

10 Arteriole

11 Smooth muscle fibers

Fig. 2. — *Transitional epithelium.*
Stain: hematoxylin-eosin. 300×.

PLATE 6

SIMPLE BRANCHED TUBULAR GLAND (DIAGRAM)

In the center of the plate a branched tubular gland with four adeno-meres has been drawn. The epithelium of the duct at its opening is continuous with the surface epithelium and is composed of columnar cells with ovoid nuclei. The glandular epithelium is cubical with flat basal nuclei.

In A a section is illustrated at the level of a-a'. There is a central orifice, the opening of the duct, which is surrounded by cells which have been cut transversally and belong to the surface epithelium.

B represents a sagittal section of the same gland, along the line b-b'. In the upper part the section has passed obliquely through the wall of the duct, and the lumen is not seen. The duct appears to be a solid column of stratified epithelium. At the bottom the section passes transversally through the adjacent adenomere, showing its circular shape, the narrow central lumen, and the number and shape of cells which form it.

C represents an oblique section of the duct along the line c-c'. The lumen has an elliptic shape and at both ends the epithelium appears as a mosaic because the cells of several levels of the duct have been cut transversally.

D represents a cross section through the wall of the adjacent adenomere and therefore appears as a solid mass of cells, of which only the peripheral ones show their nuclei.

E represents two adenomeres, the upper sectioned obliquely, the lower sectioned transversally.

F represents three adenomeres cut transversally. Each shows the narrow central lumen and the cuboid cells forming the wall.

G represents an adenomere cut longitudinally through the lumen except at the upper part where the wall has been sectioned obliquely.

PLATE 6

TUBULAR GLAND (DIAGRAM)

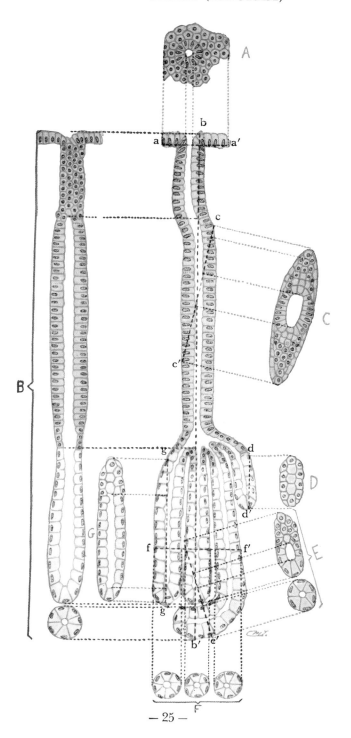

PLATE 7

COMPOUND ACINOUS GLAND (DIAGRAM)

In the center of the plate, a longitudinal section of the gland has been drawn. The glandular duct with its branches, and several adenomeres, rounded or slightly lengthened, can be seen.

A, B and C show the adenomeres, all having an outer spherical shape, sectioned through planes a-a', b-b', and c-c' respectively. The fact that the lumen of each terminal sac is narrow, classifies the gland as acinous, in contrast to the larger lumen of alveolar glands (cf. plate 8). The entire gland illustrated is, with its ramified duct, a compound acinous gland.

Compound glands composed of both tubular and acinous adenomeres are known as tubuloacinous glands.

PLATE 7

COMPOUND ACINOUS GLAND (DIAGRAM)

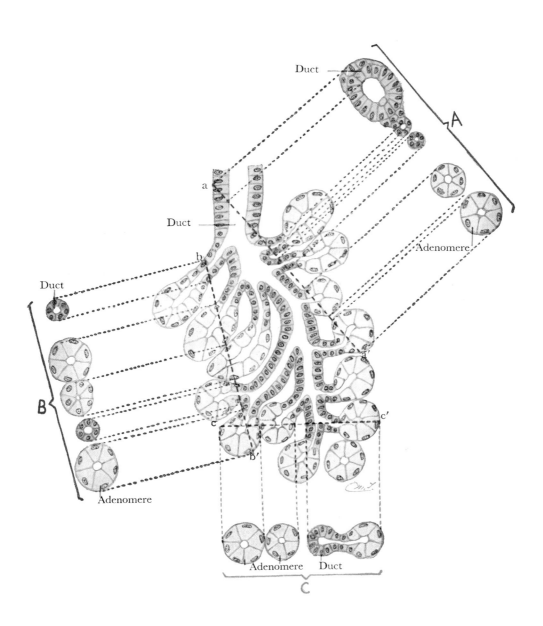

PLATE 8

COMPOUND ALVEOLAR GLAND (DIAGRAM)

An alveolar gland has spherical adenomeres, each with a large lumen (cf. plate 7, acinous gland). This can be seen in longitudinal and in transverse sections.

In A, an alveolus is shown which apparently has no lumen because the section a-a' has passed through the wall of the alveolus. A ramified alveolus with a partition between contiguous glandular cavities is also shown.

In B, another ramified alveolus is shown in which the section b-b' passes through the center of the cavity, far from the dividing septum.

PLATE 8
COMPOUND ALVEOLAR GLAND (DIAGRAM)

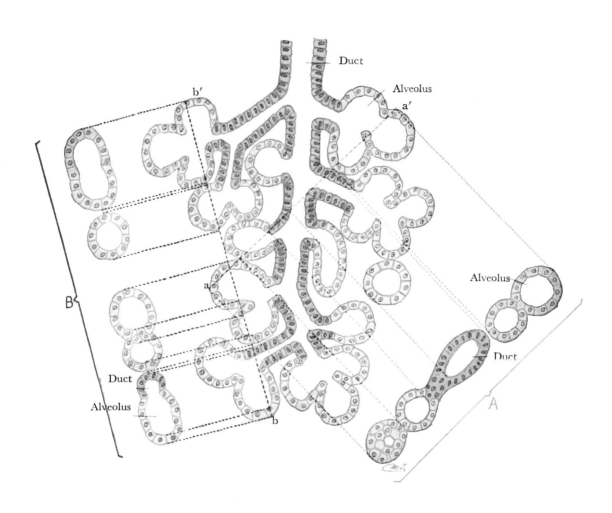

Plate 9

LOOSE (IRREGULARLY ARRANGED)
CONNECTIVE TISSUE: SPREAD

The plate illustrates subcutaneous connective tissue from a white rat, stained by the injection of a dilute solution of neutral red in normal saline.

Fibers and cells can be seen. Collagenous fibers (2, 9) are the more numerous; they are thick, wavy, and have a fibrillar constitution; no free ends or anastomoses are observed. There are also elastic fibers (1, 10); they are fine and, although unstained like the collagenous fibers, they are highly refringent. They branch out and anastomose with one another. They are not wavy but straight, except where they have been cut, in which case they are extremely flexuous.

There are many cells of varied aspect. Histiocytes, or fixed macrophages (4, 11, II) are of an irregular shape with many prolongations; in their cytoplasm there are several vacuoles filled with neutral red. Fibroblasts (8, I) are similar to histiocytes, but differ from them because they have no vacuoles containing neutral red, or only a few small ones if the stain has been acting for a long time. The nucleus is less visible than that of the histiocytes and sometimes contains one or more nucleoli (I). Mast cells (7, III) are round or polyhedral and are full of granules stained brick-red. They are seen isolated or grouped together, frequently in the neighborhood of a blood vessel. Adipose cells (3) appear as bright spheres of variable size, forming more or less numerous groups. There are also eosinophilic leukocytes, with bright unstained granules and lobulated nuclei (5), and lymphocytes, smaller than the eosinophils, with a round nucleus and little, scarcely visible protoplasm (6).

These cells and fibers are embedded in a ground substance which has been infiltrated by the injected fluid and does not appear in the picture.

A capillary (12) containing a few red cells is also seen.

PLATE 9

LOOSE (IRREGULARLY ARRANGED) CONNECTIVE TISSUE: SPREAD

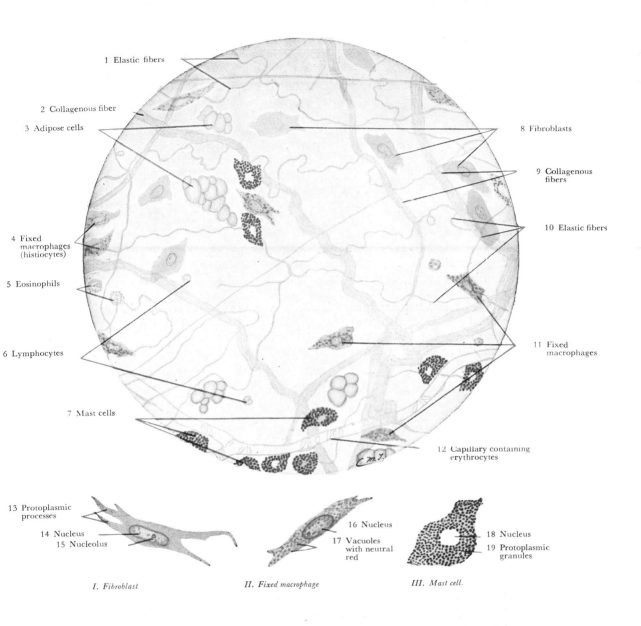

1 Elastic fibers

2 Collagenous fiber

3 Adipose cells

4 Fixed macrophages (histiocytes)

5 Eosinophils

6 Lymphocytes

7 Mast cells

8 Fibroblasts

9 Collagenous fibers

10 Elastic fibers

11 Fixed macrophages

12 Capillary containing erythrocytes

13 Protoplasmic processes

14 Nucleus
15 Nucleolus

16 Nucleus

17 Vacuoles with neutral red

18 Nucleus

19 Protoplasmic granules

I. Fibroblast

II. Fixed macrophage

III. Mast cell.

Supravital staining with neutral red. 320×.

PLATE 10 (Fig. 1)

LOOSE (IRREGULARLY ARRANGED) CONNECTIVE TISSUE

A section of submucosa of the esophagus is illustrated.

Numerous cells of irregular shape are seen, each with protoplasmic processes and an oval nucleus. The majority are fibroblasts (1). There are also histiocytes, but in this type of preparation they are not easy to recognize as such. The illustration also shows: lymphocytes (2), each with a round dark nucleus and little protoplasm; polymorphonuclear leukocytes (3) larger than the former and with lobulated nuclei; and large adipose cells (11), each with an eccentrically placed flat nucleus. The fat droplet, which each adipose cell normally contains, has disappeared owing to the method of preparation. The resulting vacuole is surrounded by a thin film of protoplasm, stained pink.

There are many small blood vessels, sectioned lengthwise or transversally. Some are capillaries (13), the wall of which is made up of an endothelial layer only. Some are venules (5, 7, 8), of a slightly larger diameter than capillaries, surrounded by a condensation of connective tissue. Some are arterioles (4, 9, 10) with smooth muscle fibers surrounding the endothelium, forming a wall of which the thickness is equivalent to the size of the lumen.

These structures are embedded in a ground-substance, stained light pink by eosin, which contains collagenous fibers (6) stained a deeper pink than the ground substance. The collagenous fibers are of varying diameters and run in different directions, forming a loosely arranged meshwork. Fine elastic fibers are also present, but are not distinguishable at this magnification.

PLATE 10 (Fig. 2)

DENSE IRREGULARLY ARRANGED CONNECTIVE TISSUE

This figure illustrates dense connective tissue from the dermis of the skin. Fibroblasts (5, 11) are less numerous than in loose connective tissue, but there are many collagenous fibers (1, 2) in large bundles cut at different angles. There are a few fine wavy elastic fibers, stained bright red by eosin (10).

There are also a few polymorphonuclear leukocytes (3), lymphocytes (9) and blood capillaries (4, 8). In the neighborhood of a blood capillary sectioned obliquely (8), there is an undifferentiated mesenchymal cell (6).

PLATE 10

CONNECTIVE TISSUE

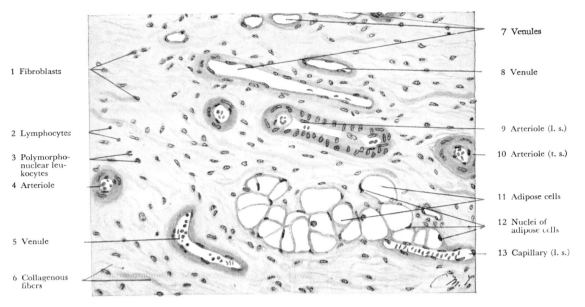

1 Fibroblasts

2 Lymphocytes

3 Polymorpho-
nuclear leu-
kocytes
4 Arteriole

5 Venule

6 Collagenous
fibers

7 Venules

8 Venule

9 Arteriole (l. s.)

10 Arteriole (t. s.)

11 Adipose cells

12 Nuclei of
adipose cells

13 Capillary (l. s.)

Fig. 1. — *Loose connective tissue.*

Stain. hematoxylin-eosin. 300×.

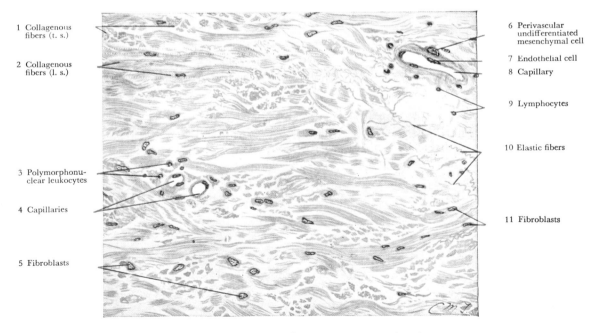

1 Collagenous
fibers (t. s.)

2 Collagenous
fibers (l. s.)

3 Polymorphonu-
clear leukocytes

4 Capillaries

5 Fibroblasts

6 Perivascular
undifferentiated
mesenchymal cell

7 Endothelial cell
8 Capillary

9 Lymphocytes

10 Elastic fibers

11 Fibroblasts

Fig. 2. — *Dense irregularly arranged connective tissue.*

Stain: hematoxylin-eosin. 300×.

PLATE 11 (Fig. 1)

MUCOUS TISSUE: WHARTON'S JELLY

Numerous stellate cells termed fibroblasts (1, 2, 3) are embedded in an abundant ground substance (5). The fibroblasts have long processes which often anastomose. The only differentiated fibers are a few collagenous fibers (4).

PLATE 11 (Fig. 2)

DENSE REGULAR CONNECTIVE TISSUE: TENDON

Numerous collagenous fibers (2) are observed; they are usually thick, with a fibrillar structure and parallel to each other. Between the bundles of these fibers (5, 6), there are rows of cells (1, 3, 4) which are flattened fibroblasts, the tendon cells, with nuclei which are ovoid (3) or rod-like (4) according to the plane in which they are visualized.

Dense regular connective tissue also forms the capsules or fibrous membranes which surround many organs, and in these locations it is sometimes referred to as dense fibrous tissue (dense collagenous tissue).

PLATE 11
CONNECTIVE TISSUE

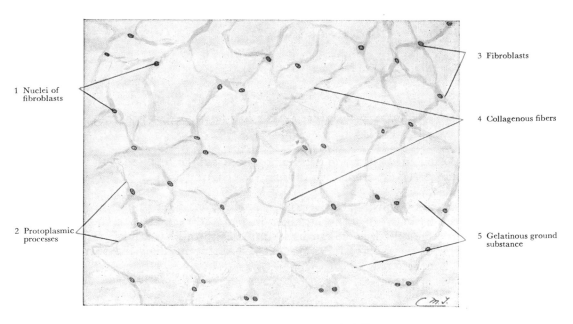

1 Nuclei of
fibroblasts

2 Protoplasmic
processes

3 Fibroblasts

4 Collagenous fibers

5 Gelatinous ground
substance

FIG. 1. — *Mucous tissue: Wharton's jelly.*
Stain: hematoxylin-eosin. 250×.

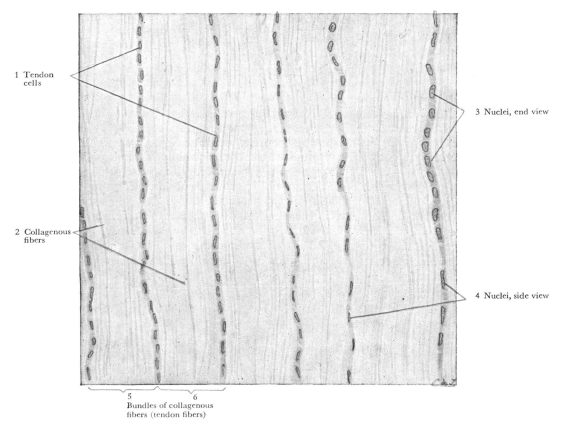

1 Tendon
cells

2 Collagenous
fibers

3 Nuclei, end view

4 Nuclei, side view

5   6
Bundles of collagenous
fibers (tendon fibers)

FIG. 2. — *Dense regular connective tissue: tendon.*
Stain: hematoxylin-eosin. 250×.

PLATE 12 (Fig. 1)

HYALINE CARTILAGE (FRESH PREPARATION)

Distributed throughout a homogenous substance, the hyaline ground substance (4), are numerous lacunae, which contain the cartilage cells or chondrocytes (1).

In normal intact cartilage the chondrocytes with granular cytoplasm fill the lacunae. In many instances in removed cartilage the chondrocytes contract and the lacunae can be seen (3). Each cell has a nucleus (2) which is seen as a small vesicle more highly refringent than the surrounding cytoplasm.

PLATE 12 (Fig. 2)

HYALINE CARTILAGE (STAINED)

This section of cartilage from the trachea has been stained, and the cartilage cells, or chondrocytes (11, 13), can be seen isolated (11) or forming isogenous groups (13) in the lacunae. Each lacuna is surrounded by a portion of basophilic ground substance, forming a territorial area or cartilage capsule (15), around one lacuna or group of lacunae. Between the groups there is a feeble basophilic ground substance forming the interterritorial area (14). The perichondrium surrounds the whole cartilage (4, 9, 17); its deeper part is the chondrogenous layer (10) containing many connective tissue cells which become converted into chondrocytes.

Connective tissue (5, 8, 18) surrounds the cartilage, and in this case, glandular alveoli (1, 7) and ducts (6) of tracheal glands.

PLATE 12

CARTILAGE

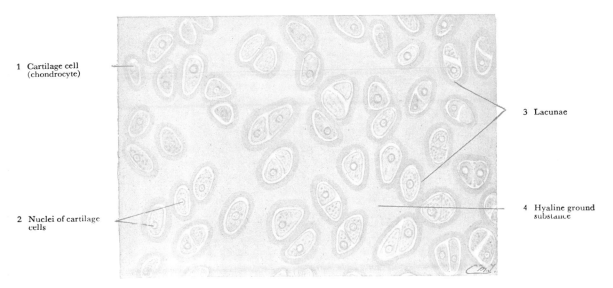

1 Cartilage cell
(chondrocyte)

3 Lacunae

4 Hyaline ground
substance

2 Nuclei of cartilage
cells

FIG. 1. — *Hyaline cartilage.*
Fresh preparation. 320×.

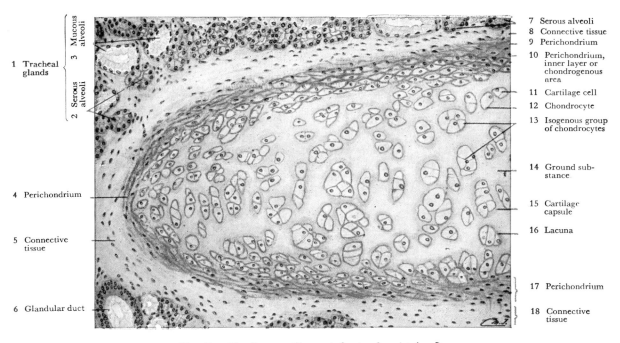

3 Mucous
alveoli

1 Tracheal
glands

2 Serous
alveoli

7 Serous alveoli
8 Connective tissue
9 Perichondrium
10 Perichondrium,
inner layer or
chondrogenous
area
11 Cartilage cell
12 Chondrocyte
13 Isogenous group
of chondrocytes

14 Ground sub-
stance

15 Cartilage
capsule

16 Lacuna

4 Perichondrium

5 Connective
tissue

6 Glandular duct

17 Perichondrium

18 Connective
tissue

FIG. 2. — *Hyaline cartilage of the trachea (stained).*
Stain: hematoxylin-eosin. 120×.

PLATE 13 (Fig. 1)

FIBROCARTILAGE: INTERVERTEBRAL DISK

There are many small chondrocytes (2, 4), usually distributed in chains (3), and surrounded by ground substance (6). Numerous collagenous fibers (5) also lie in the ground substance; presence of these fibers is characteristic of this type of cartilage.

Each chondrocyte contains a deeply stained round central nucleus (2). Each chondrocyte, or group of chondrocytes, lies in a well-defined lacuna (1).

PLATE 13 (Fig. 2)

ELASTIC CARTILAGE: EPIGLOTTIS

The cartilage cells (4) are usually large, but smaller chondrocytes (2) may be seen in the deep layers of the perichondrium. Staining with orcein shows up many elastic fibers in the ground substance (1), this being the characteristic structure of elastic cartilage. These fibers vary in their diameter, some are of considerable thickness. The chondrocytes do not fill the lacunae, being partially retracted; the nucleus (5) is often eccentrically placed.

The perichondrium (3) also has many elastic fibers, which frequently are continuous with the elastic fibers of the cartilage.

PLATE 13

CARTILAGE

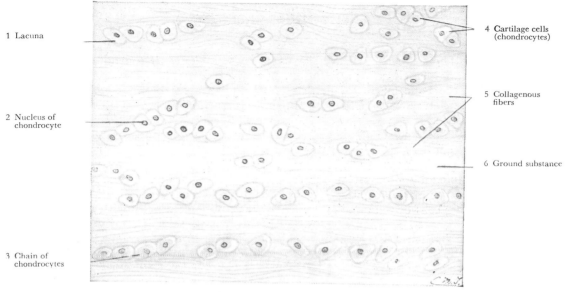

1 Lacuna

2 Nucleus of
chondrocyte

3 Chain of
chondrocytes

4 Cartilage cells
(chondrocytes)

5 Collagenous
fibers

6 Ground substance

FIG. 1. — *Fibrocartilage: intervertebral disk.*
Stain: hematoxylin-eosin. 320×.

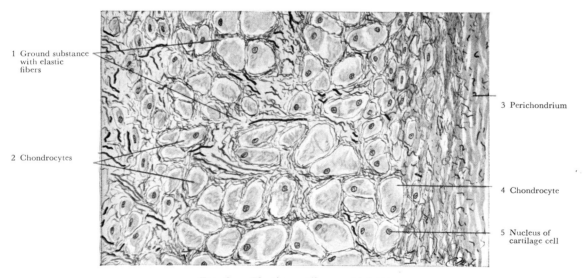

1 Ground substance
with elastic
fibers

2 Chondrocytes

3 Perichondrium

4 Chondrocyte

5 Nucleus of
cartilage cell

FIG. 2. — *Elastic cartilage: epiglottis.*
Stain: hematoxylin-orcein. 320×.

PLATE 14 (Fig. 1)

COMPACT BONE, DRIED: DIAPHYSIS OF THE TIBIA
(TRANSVERSE SECTION)

There are many Haversian systems (4, 8) between the outer circumferential lamellae (10) and the inner circumferential lamellae (6) surrounding the bone marrow canal. The triangular areas between neighboring Haversian systems are filled by interstitial lamellae (7, 9), also called ground lamellae.

The lamellae (3) have numerous lenticular cavities, or lacunae (1, 11, 15), each of which in living bone is occupied by a bone cell, or osteocyte. From each lacuna radiate fine canaliculi (12), which in living bone are occupied by protoplasmic processes of the osteocytes. These canaliculi anastomose with neighboring canaliculi and with the canaliculi of neighboring cells of the same Haversian system, but not usually with canaliculi of adjacent Haversian systems. Each Haversian system is clearly separated from its neighbors by a homogeneous, bright layer of cement (5). Each Haversian system encloses an Haversian canal (14), which contains a blood vessel in living bone.

Most of the Haversian canals have been sectioned transversally, but some of them may be cut obliquely (8). The canals may anastomose (13) or they may branch (5 in Fig. 2).

PLATE 14 (Fig. 2)

COMPACT BONE, DRIED: DIAPHYSIS OF THE TIBIA
(LONGITUDINAL SECTION)

This picture represents a small area of a longitudinal section of bone shaft.

Each Haversian canal (3) is seen as a tube sectioned parallel to its axis and surrounded by numerous lamellae (1) between which are found the lenticular cavities (lacunae) (4) with their canaliculi (6).

Layers of cement (2) separate the Haversian systems from each other and are usually placed parallel to the corresponding canals. Ramification of Haversian canals is shown (5).

PLATE 14

COMPACT BONE, DRIED

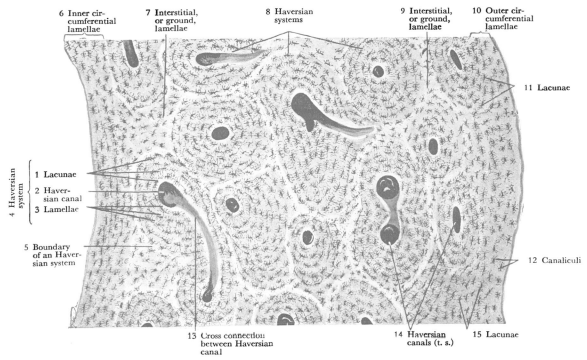

6 Inner cir-
cumferential
lamellae

7 Interstitial,
or ground,
lamellae

8 Haversian
systems

9 Interstitial,
or ground,
lamellae

10 Outer cir-
cumferential
lamellae

11 Lacunae

4 Haversian system

1 Lacunae

2 Haver-
sian canal

3 Lamellae

5 Boundary
of an Haver-
sian system

12 Canaliculi

13 Cross connection
between Haversian
canal

14 Haversian
canals (t. s.)

15 Lacunae

FIG. 1. — *Diaphysis of the tibia (transverse section).*
Stain: aniline blue. 80×.

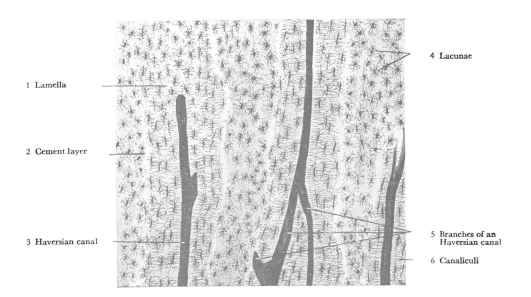

1 Lamella

2 Cement layer

3 Haversian canal

4 Lacunae

5 Branches of an
Haversian canal

6 Canaliculi

FIG. 2. — *Diaphysis of the tibia (longitudinal section).*
Stain: aniline blue. 80×.

PLATE 15 (Fig. 1)

CANCELLOUS BONE: ADULT STERNUM
(TRANSVERSE SECTION, DECALCIFIED)

Cancellous bone consists primarily of slender, bony trabeculae which ramify and anastomose (6), and enclose irregular marrow cavities of various sizes (5). Peripherally, these trabeculae merge with a thin shell of compact bone (3) in which may be observed scattered Haversian systems (4, 7). The surrounding periosteum (2) may dip into the bone at intervals. It merges with adjacent loose connective tissue (1) which is rich in blood vessels.

Except for concentric lamellae in the Haversian systems (7), the peripheral rim of bone and the trabeculae are composed of parallel lamellae, which (in this figure) are more apparent on the margins of the bony areas (8). Lacunae with osteocytes (9) are present throughout the bone.

The framework of reticular connective tissue of the marrow cavities is obscured by adipose cells (10) and groups of hemopoietic cells (11). Arteries may be seen, but sinusoids are not distinguishable in this illustration. Marrow fills the cavities, but a thin endosteum of condensed stroma becomes visible when marrow is mechanically separated from the bone (12).

PLATE 15 (Fig. 2)

INTRAMEMBRANOUS BONE FORMATION
(MANDIBLE OF A FETUS OF FIVE MONTHS, DECALCIFIED)

The upper part of the section shows the gum covering the developing mandible. The mucosa of the gum consists of stratified squamous epithelium (1) and a wide lamina propria (2) with blood vessels and nerves.

Below the lamina propria is seen the bony tissue in the process of development. The periosteum (3) is differentiated, and numerous anastomosing trabeculae constitute the bone. These trabeculae surround primitive marrow cavities of various sizes (14). The primitive marrow consists of embryonic connective tissue with blood vessels and nerves (16). At the periphery of the bone, collagenous fibers of the inner periosteum are in continuity with the fibrils of the embryonic connective tissue of adjacent marrow cavities (6) and with collagenous fibers within the bony trabeculae (10).

In close contact with some of the developing trabeculae are seen osteoblasts (7, 15) in linear arrangement, associated with bone deposition, and osteoclasts (5, 8), which are multinucleated giant cells related to the process of bone resorption.

Within the bony trabeculae are osteocytes in their lacunae (4, 9). Although collagenous fibers embedded in the bony matrix are obscured, the continuity with fibers of the embryonic connective tissue in the marrow cavities may be seen at the margins of many trabeculae (13).

It should be noted that formation of new bone is not constantly in progress. Many inactive areas are present, where bone deposition has ceased temporarily: neither osteoid nor osteoblasts are present. In some of the primitive marrow cavities, fibroblasts are enlarging preparatory to differentiating to osteoblasts (12). Elsewhere, osteoid may be seen on the margins of the bony trabeculae (11, 17); osteoblasts may (11) or may not be present (17). Definitive myeloid tissue is not yet present in the marrow cavities.

PLATE 15

FIG. 1. CANCELLOUS BONE: ADULT STERNUM (TRANSVERSE SECTION, DECALCIFIED)

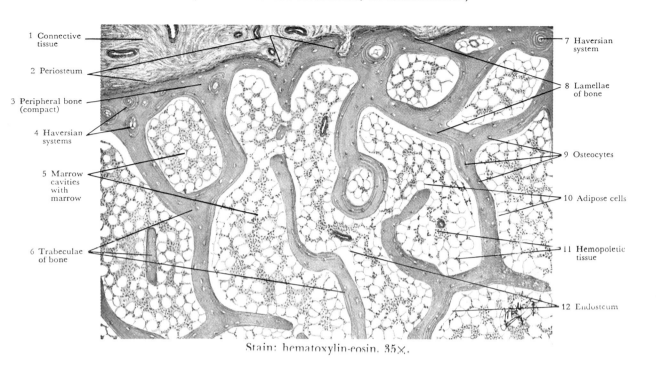

1 Connective tissue
2 Periosteum
3 Peripheral bone (compact)
4 Haversian systems
5 Marrow cavities with marrow
6 Trabeculae of bone
7 Haversian system
8 Lamellae of bone
9 Osteocytes
10 Adipose cells
11 Hemopoietic tissue
12 Endosteum

Stain: hematoxylin-eosin. 35×.

FIG. 2. INTRAMEMBRANOUS BONE FORMATION: MANDIBLE OF A FETUS OF FIVE MONTHS (TRANSVERSE SECTION, DECALCIFIED)

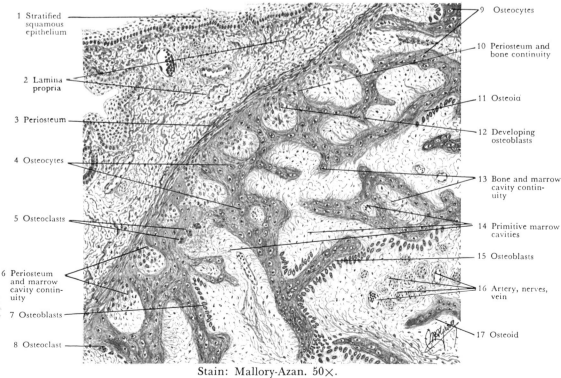

1 Stratified squamous epithelium
2 Lamina propria
3 Periosteum
4 Osteocytes
5 Osteoclasts
6 Periosteum and marrow cavity continuity
7 Osteoblasts
8 Osteoclast
9 Osteocytes
10 Periosteum and bone continuity
11 Osteoid
12 Developing osteoblasts
13 Bone and marrow cavity continuity
14 Primitive marrow cavities
15 Osteoblasts
16 Artery, nerves, vein
17 Osteoid

Stain: Mallory-Azan. 50×.

PLATE 16

INTRACARTILAGINOUS BONE FORMATION: DEVELOPING METACARPAL BONE (PANORAMIC VIEW, LONGITUDINAL SECTION)

This illustration shows endochondral or intracartilaginous bone formation, in which the future bone is first formed as a plate of embryonic hyaline cartilage. The cartilage is then gradually destroyed and replaced by bone. In the center of the shaft of the bone illustrated, this has already occurred, and in addition, most of the original spongy bone so formed has been destroyed and resorbed to form the central marrow cavity, thus leaving only scattered, thin trabeculae of bone of endochondral origin (11, 30). Red marrow (13) fills the cavity. The stroma of reticular connective tissue is obscured by masses of developing erythrocytes and granulocytes, mature forms of these, megakaryocytes (14) and numerous venous sinuses (12) and capillaries, as well as other blood vessels.

The process of continued endochondral bone formation can be followed from the upper part of the illustration downward toward the central marrow cavity. Uppermost is seen the zone of reserve normal hyaline cartilage (17) in which the chondrocytes in their lacunae are distributed singly or in small groups (2). Chondrocytes then multiply rapidly and become arranged in columns of cells (3, 18); cells and lacunae increase in size toward the lower area of this zone of proliferating cartilage (19). These chondrocytes then hypertrophy by swelling of nucleus and cytoplasm, lacunae enlarge (4), the cells then degenerate and the thin partitions of intervening matrix calcify (20). The calcified cartilage stains a deep purple.

Tufts of vascular marrow penetrate into this area (5, 21), erode the lacunar walls and calcified cartilage (5, 21), thus forming new, small marrow spaces. Osteoblasts are differentiated, osteoid and bone are deposited around remaining spicules of calcified cartilage (6). This is the zone of ossification (21).

The lower, lateral two-thirds of the illustration shows the development of periosteal bone. Osteoblasts become differentiated from embryonic fibroblasts in the inner layer of the periosteum (9) and a bone collar is formed (10) by the intramembranous method. Formation of new periosteal bone keeps pace with formation of new endochondral bone (22). The bone collar increases in thickness and compactness as development of the bone proceeds, the greatest thickness at any time being in the central part of the diaphysis at the initial site of formation of periosteal bone (29) around the primary ossification center.

Surrounding the shaft of the developing bone are soft tissues, muscle (7), subcutaneous layer and dermis of the skin (15, 25), with hair follicles (26), sebaceous glands (28) and sweat glands (16), and the epidermis (24).

PLATE 16

INTRACARTILAGINOUS BONE FORMATION: DEVELOPING METACARPAL BONE (PANORAMIC VIEW, LONGITUDINAL SECTION)

1 Perichondrium

2 Chondrocytes
in lacunae

3 Column of
chondrocytes

4 Hypertrophied
chondrocytes
and calcified
matrix

5 Vascular tufts
of osteogenic
marrow

6 Osteoid and
bone tissue
around a
spicule of
calcified cartilage

7 Muscle

8 Periosteum
(outer
layer)

9 Periosteum
(inner layer
with
osteoblasts)

10 Periosteal
bone
(bone collar)

11 Bone trabeculae
of endochondral
origin

12 Venous sinusoid

13 Red bone
marrow with
myeloid elements

14 Megakaryocytes

15 Subcutaneous
connective tissue
and dermis

16 Sweat
gland

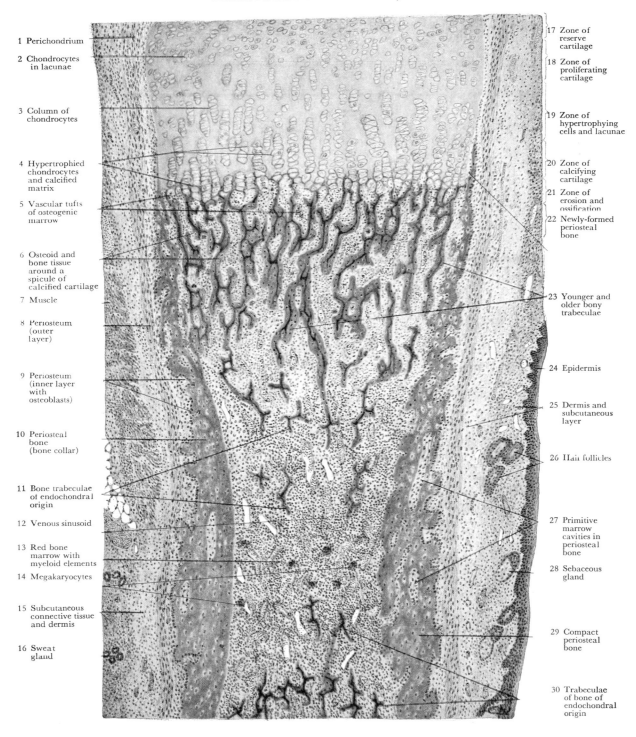

17 Zone of
reserve
cartilage

18 Zone of
proliferating
cartilage

19 Zone of
hypertrophying
cells and lacunae

20 Zone of
calcifying
cartilage

21 Zone of
erosion and
ossification

22 Newly-formed
periosteal
bone

23 Younger and
older bony
trabeculae

24 Epidermis

25 Dermis and
subcutaneous
layer

26 Hair follicles

27 Primitive
marrow
cavities in
periosteal
bone

28 Sebaceous
gland

29 Compact
periosteal
bone

30 Trabeculae
of bone of
endochondral
origin

Stain: hematoxylin-eosin. 60×.

PLATE 17

INTRACARTILAGINOUS BONE FORMATION
(SECTIONAL VIEW)

This preparation shows, in more detail, the processes involved in endochondral bone formation at the zone of ossification and adjacent areas, corresponding approximately to 3 through 6 in Plate 16.

Proliferating chondroblasts are arranged in columns (2, 10). The cells in the lower part of this zone hypertrophy because of accumulation of glycogen in their cytoplasm and swelling of their nuclei, and lacunae hypertrophy simultaneously. Cytoplasm then becomes vacuolated, nuclei become pyknotic (3), the thin partitions of cartilaginous matrix become calcified (4, 11).

Sprouts of vascular marrow invading this area (5) produce the zone of erosion. Osteoblasts are formed, line up along remaining spicules of calcified cartilage (14) and lay down osteoid (15) and bone. Osteoblasts entrapped in the osteoid or bone become osteocytes (7).

In the marrow (17) are seen cells belonging to the erythrocytic (18) and granulocytic (19) series, and megakaryocytes (8). Multinucleated osteoclasts (16) are shown adjacent to bone tissue which is being resorbed. They lie in depressions, Howship's lacunae.

On the right side of the illustration is an area of periosteal cancellous bone (13) with osteocytes and primitive marrow cavities. New bone is being added peripherally by osteoblasts derived from primitive fibroblasts of the inner periosteum (12). The outer layer of the periosteum continues upward as the perichondrium (9).

PLATE 17

INTRACARTILAGINOUS BONE FORMATION (SECTIONAL VIEW)

1 Basophilic ground substance (matrix)

2 Columns of cartilage cells

3 Hypertrophied cartilage cells (vacuolized cytoplasm, pyknotic nuclei)

4 Degenerating cartilage cells surrounded by calcified matrix

5 Invading capillaries and embryonic bone marrow in zone of erosion

6 Spicule of calcified cartilage surrounded by osteoid

7 Newly-formed osteocytes

8 Megakaryocytes

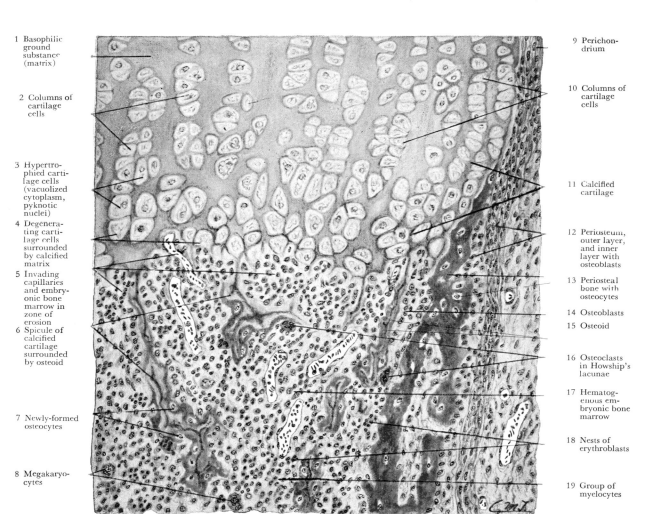

9 Perichondrium

10 Columns of cartilage cells

11 Calcified cartilage

12 Periosteum, outer layer, and inner layer with osteoblasts

13 Periosteal bone with osteocytes

14 Osteoblasts

15 Osteoid

16 Osteoclasts in Howship's lacunae

17 Hematogenous embryonic bone marrow

18 Nests of erythroblasts

19 Group of myelocytes

Stain: hematoxylin-eosin. 200×.

PLATE 18

FORMATION OF BONE: DEVELOPMENT OF
HAVERSIAN SYSTEMS (DECALCIFIED, TRANSVERSE SECTION)

This represents a late stage of development in a future compact bone. Primitive Haversian systems have already formed and others are in the process of developing. In a metacarpal bone, such as seen in Plate 16, or in a long bone, the first compact bone will have formed by subperiosteal deposition (Plate 16, 29). Vascular sprouts of connective tissue from the periosteum or endosteum will have eroded this bone to form primitive Haversian systems, as seen in this illustration. Reconstruction will continue by breakdown of these first (and later) Haversian systems and formation of new ones.

In this plate, we see a thick wall of immature compact bone; the ground substance (11) is deeply stained by eosin. Primitive Haversian systems are seen in transverse sections, with large Haversian canals (8) surrounded by concentric lamellae of bone (3) and their contained osteocytes (1). The Haversian canals contain primitive connective tissue and one or more blood vessels (6, 8). Deposition of bone is continuing in some of these, as indicated by osteoblasts at the periphery of the Haversian canal (8, lower line; 9, upper line). Osteoclasts (2) indicate resorption of some of these Haversian systems, preparatory to subsequent reconstruction.

A longitudinal channel of osteogenic connective tissue (10) passes through the bone. From it arise tufts of vascular connective tissue which are Haversian canals in the process of formation (4). Osteoblasts are already lined up on the periphery.

In the lower part of the plate is the large, central marrow cavity filled with bone marrow (14). Osteoclasts (13) in Howship's lacunae (12), megakaryocytes (16), blood vessels (7) and a spicule of bone (15) are illustrated.

In a compact bone which has developed by the intramembranous method, most of the Haversian systems are probably formed by deposition of bony lamellae inwardly around small marrow cavities, the resulting small canal becoming the Haversian canal. The bone illustrated here is actually such a bone, the inferior portion of the maxilla.

PLATE 18

FORMATION OF BONE: DEVELOPMENT OF HAVERSIAN SYSTEMS (DECALCIFIED, TRANSVERSE SECTION)

1. Heterop
   myelocy

2. Nucleu:
   adipose
   cell.

3. Basophi
   erythrol

4. Eosinop
   myelocy

5. Megaka
   cyte.

6. Erythro

7. Plasma
   cell.

8. Reticula
   stroma.

9. Arteriol

10. Venule
    with ery
    rocytes :
    leucocyt
    in lumer

11. Primitiv
    reticular
    cells.

1. Primitive
   reticular
   cells.

2. Reticulo-
   endothelial c

3. Venous
   sinusoid.

4. Basophilic
   erythroblast:

5. Venous
   sinusoid witl
   erythrocytes

6. Orthochro-
   matic eryth-
   roblasts.

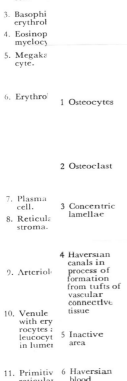

1 Osteocytes

2 Osteoclast

3 Concentric
  lamellae

4 Haversian
  canals in
  process of
  formation
  from tufts of
  vascular
  connective
  tissue

5 Inactive
  area

6 Haversian
  blood
  vessel

7 Venous sinusoids
  in the bone
  marrow

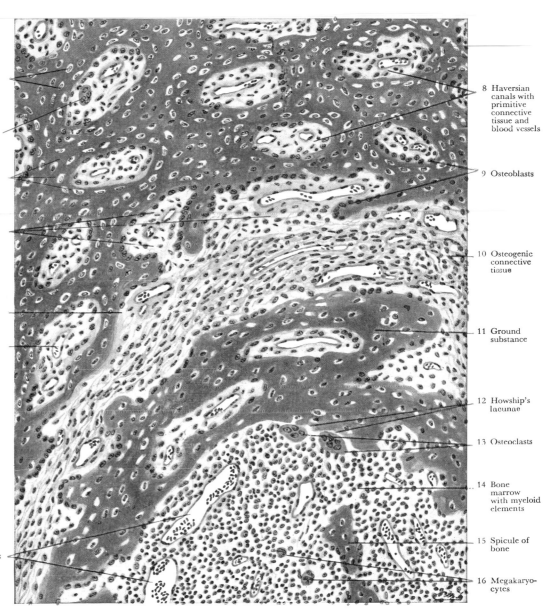

8 Haversian
  canals with
  primitive
  connective
  tissue and
  blood vessels

9 Osteoblasts

10 Osteogenic
   connective
   tissue

11 Ground
   substance

12 Howship's
   lacunae

13 Osteoclasts

14 Bone
   marrow
   with myeloid
   elements

15 Spicule of
   bone

16 Megakaryo-
   cytes

Stain: hematoxylin-eosin. 140×.

PLATE 25 (Fig. 1)

GRAY MATTER (ANTERIOR HORN OF THE SPINAL CORD)

Large cells each with a vesicular nucleus (6) are motor neurons of the spinal cord. Their cytoplasm contains a large number of granules (Nissl bodies or tigroid substance) (11) deeply stained by basic aniline, giving the cell a spotted appearance. Many cell processes containing the Nissl bodies are dendrites (7, 8). The one cell process which has no Nissl bodies is the axon (1), nor are there any such bodies in the cytoplasm at which the axon originates; this is termed the axon hillock (4). The nucleus contains a large deeply stained nucleolus (5, 12) and a fine chromatin reticulum with wide meshes (13).

Many nuclei of neuroglial cells (2, 10, 15, 16) are visible; the cytoplasm of these cells is not stained. Round nuclei with a loose network of chromatin belong to protoplasmic astrocytes (2, 16); smaller round nuclei, which stain more deeply, belong to oligodendrocytes (15); and elongated dark nuclei to microglia (10).

Some of the capillaries show the stained nuclei of their endothelial cells (9).

PLATE 25 (Fig. 2)

GRAY MATTER (ANTERIOR HORN OF THE SPINAL CORD)

This preparation has been made by silver impregnation. The cytoplasm and cell processes (3) contain numerous neurofibrils (2, 13), which are not shown in the previous illustration. The nuclei appear as clear spaces, lightly stained; sometimes a well-stained nucleolus is visible (15).

Between the cells there are many fibrillar cell processes, coming from other nerve cells or from neuroglial cells.

Nuclei of neuroglial cells are seen (1, 4, 5, 8, 9, 10), showing characteristics as described in Fig. 1 above.

PLATE 25

NERVOUS TISSUE

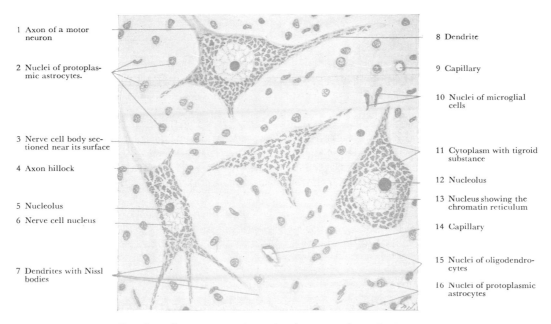

1 Axon of a motor neuron

2 Nuclei of protoplasmic astrocytes.

3 Nerve cell body sectioned near its surface

4 Axon hillock

5 Nucleolus
6 Nerve cell nucleus

7 Dendrites with Nissl bodies

8 Dendrite

9 Capillary

10 Nuclei of microglial cells

11 Cytoplasm with tigroid substance

12 Nucleolus

13 Nucleus showing the chromatin reticulum

14 Capillary

15 Nuclei of oligodendrocytes

16 Nuclei of protoplasmic astrocytes

FIG. 1. — *Gray matter (anterior horn of the spinal cord).*
Nissl's method. 350×.

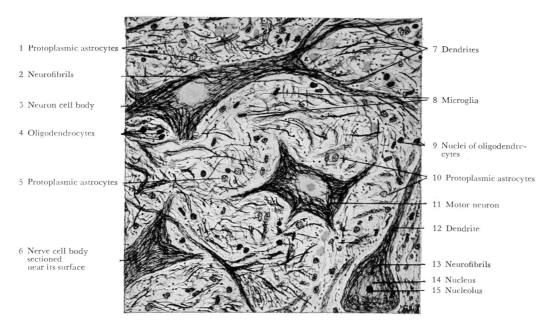

1 Protoplasmic astrocytes

2 Neurofibrils

3 Neuron cell body

4 Oligodendrocytes

5 Protoplasmic astrocytes

6 Nerve cell body sectioned near its surface

7 Dendrites

8 Microglia

9 Nuclei of oligodendrocytes

10 Protoplasmic astrocytes

11 Motor neuron

12 Dendrite

13 Neurofibrils
14 Nucleus
15 Nucleolus

FIG. 2. — *Gray matter (anterior horn of the spinal cord).*
Cajal's method. 350×.

PLATE 26 (Fig. 1)

GRAY MATTER (ANTERIOR HORN OF THE SPINAL CORD)

The nerve cells are stained dark brown (4); their processes can be traced to their finest branches (2). Structural details seen in Plate 25 are not seen here, because a different staining method was employed.

Several protoplasmic astrocytes (1, 3) are illustrated, with deeply stained cytoplasm and cell processes.

PLATE 26 (Fig. 2)

GRAY MATTER (ANTERIOR HORN OF THE SPINAL CORD)

The intercellular space is filled by numerous nerve fibers of varying sizes (2, 5) and fine processes of neuroglia cells. Cells shown in other illustrations of nervous tissue are here either not seen or are stained a pale yellow.

PLATE 26

NERVOUS TISSUE

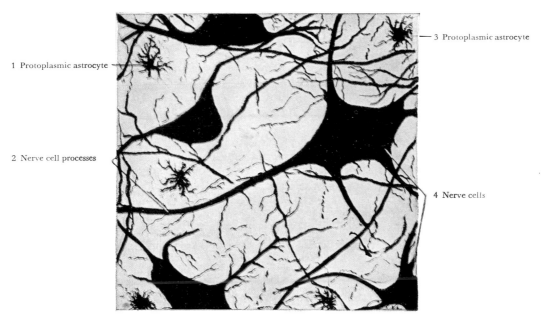

1 Protoplasmic astrocyte

2 Nerve cell processes

3 Protoplasmic astrocyte

4 Nerve cells

FIG. 1. — *Gray matter (anterior horn of the spinal cord).*
Golgi's method. 350×.

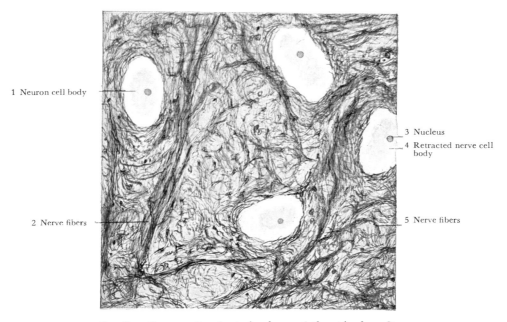

1 Neuron cell body

2 Nerve fibers

3 Nucleus

4 Retracted nerve cell body

5 Nerve fibers

FIG. 2. — *Gray matter (anterior horn of the spinal cord).*
Modified Weigert-Pal method. 350×.

PLATE 27 (Fig. 1)

FIBROUS ASTROCYTES OF THE BRAIN

In the center of the preparation, stained by del Rio Hortega's method for astrocytes (*i.e.*, macroglia), a stellate cell with fibrillar structure and processes radiating from the cell body can be seen (5). One of the processes ends on a small blood vessel (4). This is a fibrous astrocyte with vascular pedicle, situated in the white matter of the brain.

In the upper part of the picture another cell (1), similar to the one described above, is seen near a blood vessel which is partly surrounded by the body and processes of the astrocyte (2). This is a perivascular fibrous astrocyte (1).

Oligodendrocyte, type I (3), with a rounded or angular cell body and nucleus are seen, but not the cell processes.

In the lower right corner a capillary (6) is shown, surrounded by reticular fibers.

PLATE 27 (Fig. 2)

OLIGODENDROCYTES OF THE BRAIN

Golgi's method, as modified by del Rio Hortega, has been used in this brain section. The following types of cells are shown:

Protoplasmic astrocyte (4), with stellate body and numerous flexuous branching processes.

Oligodendrocyte, type I (5), with a rounded or angular cell body and a few fine varicose processes with only a few branches.

Oligodendrocyte, type II (2), of similar form, except that the processes are noticeably thicker.

PLATE 27 (Fig. 3)

MICROGLIA OF THE BRAIN

Del Rio Hortega's method for microglia has been used. Small cell bodies with numerous branching processes are seen. The surface of the cell body and processes have a characteristic "spiny" aspect (1, 4). They are microglial cells, which arise from the mesoderm (mesoglia); some authorities do not consider them to be part of the neuroglia.

Capillaries and a nerve cell body are visible.

PLATE 27

NEUROGLIA

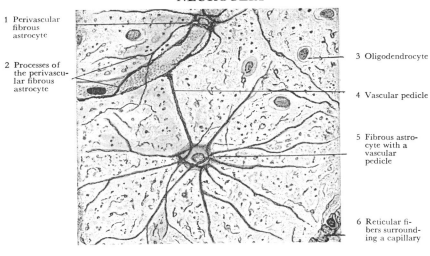

1 Perivascular fibrous astrocyte

2 Processes of the perivascular fibrous astrocyte

3 Oligodendrocyte

4 Vascular pedicle

5 Fibrous astrocyte with a vascular pedicle

6 Reticular fibers surrounding a capillary

FIG. 1. — *Fibrous astrocytes of the brain.*
Del Rio Hortega's method.

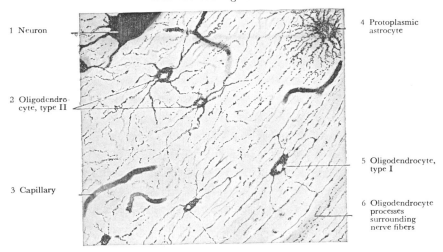

1 Neuron

2 Oligodendrocyte, type II

3 Capillary

4 Protoplasmic astrocyte

5 Oligodendrocyte, type I

6 Oligodendrocyte processes surrounding nerve fibers

FIG. 2. — *Oligodendrocytes of the brain.*

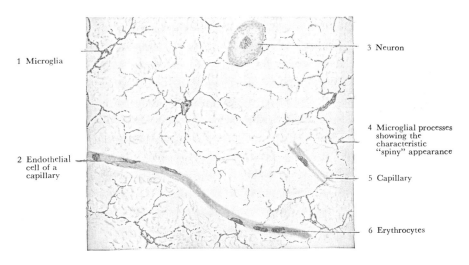

1 Microglia

2 Endothelial cell of a capillary

3 Neuron

4 Microglial processes showing the characteristic "spiny" appearance

5 Capillary

6 Erythrocytes

FIG. 3. — *Microglia of the brain.*
Del Rio Hortega's method.

PLATE 28 (Fig. 1)

MYELINATED NERVE FIBERS (DISSOCIATED)

A portion of the sciatic nerve of a toad has been treated with osmic acid and teased apart. Its constituent fibers appear as fine filaments, stained black by reduction of osmic acid where myelin is present. The myelin sheath is seen as a thick dark line on the periphery of the fibers (4); at intervals it is discontinued, forming the nodes of Ranvier (1, 6). At the nodes the fiber consists only of the unstained axon (2, 5, 7) surrounded by the neurolemma or Schwann's sheath. The neurolemma envelops the full length of the fiber but is not demonstrated by the staining method used. The myelin sheath in the internodal segments shows many oblique unstained lines known as the Schmidt-Lantermann clefts (3, 8).

PLATE 28 (Fig. 2)

NERVE (TRANSVERSE SECTION)

Several bundles (fasciculi) of nerve fibers have been sectioned obliquely (8) or transversally (1). They are clearly separated from the neighboring connective tissue by the perineurium (2) which surrounds them. Delicate lamellae of connective tissue arise in the perineurium and penetrate between the fibers of each fasciculus; these fibers are known as the endoneurium (5). Among the nerve cell fibers there are many nuclei belonging to cells forming the neurolemma (Schwann's sheath) (3) or to cells of the endoneurium (5). In the connective tissue (17) between the fasciculi an artery is seen, with its muscular coat (12), inner elastic layer (14), endothelium (15) and the adventitia with nutritional vessels (13). There are also arteries of smaller diameter sectioned transversally or obliquely (6, 10), venules (16), capillaries (18), and adipose cells (7, 19).

PLATE 28

NERVOUS TISSUE

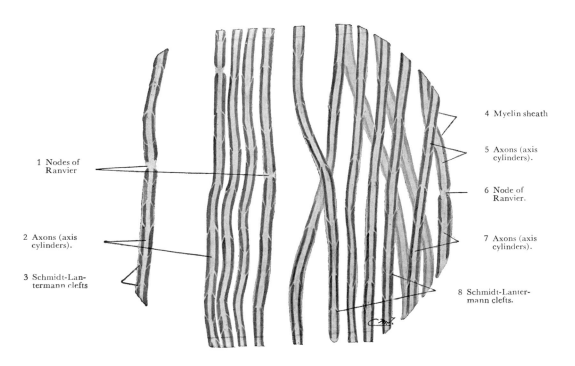

1 Nodes of
Ranvier

2 Axons (axis
cylinders).

3 Schmidt-Lan-
termann clefts

4 Myelin sheath

5 Axons (axis
cylinders).

6 Node of
Ranvier.

7 Axons (axis
cylinders).

8 Schmidt-Lanter-
mann clefts.

FIG. 1. — *Myelinated nerve fibers (dissociated).*
Stain: osmic acid. 220×.

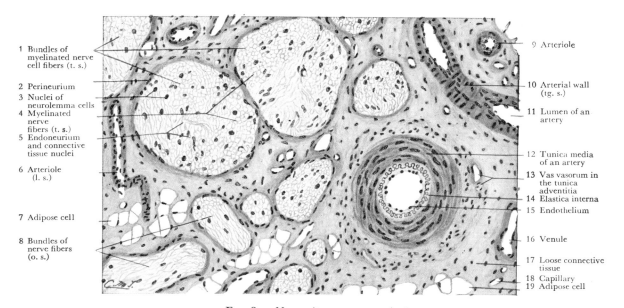

1 Bundles of
myelinated nerve
cell fibers (t. s.)

2 Perineurium
3 Nuclei of
neurolemma cells
4 Myelinated
nerve
fibers (t. s.)
5 Endoneurium
and connective
tissue nuclei

6 Arteriole
(l. s.)

7 Adipose cell

8 Bundles of
nerve fibers
(o. s.)

9 Arteriole

10 Arterial wall
(tg. s.)

11 Lumen of an
artery

12 Tunica media
of an artery
13 Vas vasorum in
the tunica
adventitia
14 Elastica interna
15 Endothelium

16 Venule

17 Loose connective
tissue
18 Capillary
19 Adipose cell

FIG. 2. — *Nerve (transverse section).*
Stain: hematoxylin-eosin. 250×.

PLATE 29

NERVOUS TISSUE: NERVES AND NERVE FIBERS

This plate illustrates the appearance of nerves and their fibers after various staining procedures.

FIG. 1. — *Nerve (panoramic view, longitudinal section)*

A portion of sciatic nerve is seen at a low magnification, as it appears in a routine preparation stained with hematoxylin-eosin. The outer part of the epineurium, of dense connective tissue, is not shown; the deeper part contains much adipose tissue (2) with many blood vessels (1). Extensions of the epineurium (3) pass between large fasciculi of nerve fibers (5). Perineurium (4) forms a dense sheath around each fasciculus. Many nuclei lined up along nerve fibers are neurolemma nuclei (Schwann cell nuclei) or nuclei of fibroblasts in the endoneurium. It is not possible to differentiate between them at this magnification.

FIG. 2. — *Nerve (longitudinal section)*

A small portion of the nerve in Fig. 1 is shown at a high magnification. The axis cylinders are seen as slender threads stained lightly with hematoxylin (1). The surrounding myelin sheath has been dissolved, leaving a distinct neurokeratin network (3). The neurolemma is not always distinguishable from surrounding connective tissue, but may be seen in places as a thin, peripheral boundary (4) and at a node of Ranvier (2) as it dips in toward the axis cylinder. Two neurolemma nuclei (Schwann cell nuclei) are seen (5). Endoneurium (sheath of Henle) (7) surrounds each fiber. It is now possible to distinguish between fibroblasts of the endoneurium (6) and neurolemma nuclei (5).

FIG. 3. — *Nerve (transverse section)*

In this transverse section of sciatic nerve, at 800 $\times$ as in Fig. 2, one sees centrally placed axis cylinders (2), the neurokeratin network (3) as radial lines which do not reach the shrunken axis cylinder, and the peripheral neurolemma (4). A neurolemma nucleus (Schwann cell nucleus) appears to encircle the nerve fiber (1).

Collagenous fibers of the endoneurium are faintly distinguishable; fibroblasts, however, are clearly seen (5). A perineurial septum (6) separates small fasciculi of nerve fibers. A small blood vessel (7) is present.

FIG. 4. — *Nerve (longitudinal section)*

This section is stained with Protargol and aniline blue. Axis cylinders (1) are prominent because of silver impregnation of the neurofibrils. The scattered black spots probably represent remnants of neurofibrils remaining after shrinkage of the axis cylinder. The neurokeratin network is not stained. Other structures are stained with aniline blue.

FIG. 5. — *Nerve (transverse section)*

As in Fig. 4, Protargol stains the axis cylinders (1), seen in cross section; the surrounding grayish area and small black droplets probably give an indication of the original diameter of the axis cylinder. Endoneurium is well demonstrated by aniline blue staining of the collagenous fibers (4, 6).

FIG. 6. — *Nerve (transverse section)*

This figure illustrates still another staining method, and also shows myelinated nerve fibers of varying sizes in a branch of the vagus nerve in the cortex of the thymus. Nuclei, axis cylinders and neurokeratin network stain red with azocarmine (1, 3, 4, 6). Endoneurium is again demonstrated clearly, especially in areas where nerve fibers are close together (7) and within groups of small nerve fibers (8).

PLATE 29
NERVOUS TISSUE: NERVES AND NERVE FIBERS

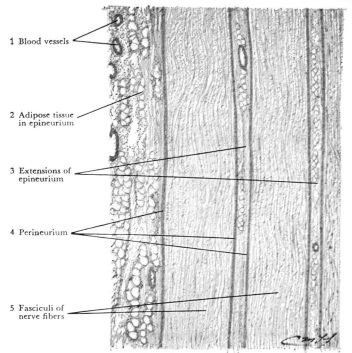

1 Blood vessels

2 Adipose tissue in epineurium

3 Extensions of epineurium

4 Perineurium

5 Fasciculi of nerve fibers

FIG. 1. — *Nerve (sciatic), panoramic view, longitudinal section.*
Stain: hematoxylin eosin. 50×.

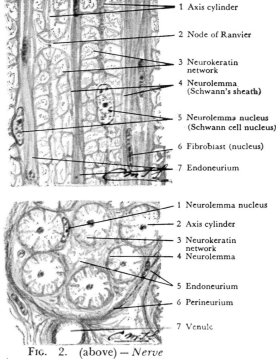

1 Axis cylinder

2 Node of Ranvier

3 Neurokeratin network

4 Neurolemma (Schwann's sheath)

5 Neurolemma nucleus (Schwann cell nucleus)

6 Fibroblast (nucleus)

7 Endoneurium

1 Neurolemma nucleus

2 Axis cylinder

3 Neurokeratin network

4 Neurolemma

5 Endoneurium

6 Perineurium

7 Venule

FIG. 2. (above) — *Nerve (sciatic), longitudinal section.*
FIG. 3. (below) — *Same, transverse section.*
Stain: hematoxylin-eosin. 800×.

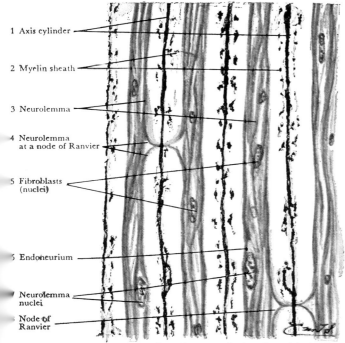

1 Axis cylinder

2 Myelin sheath

3 Neurolemma

4 Neurolemma at a node of Ranvier

5 Fibroblasts (nuclei)

6 Endoneurium

7 Neurolemma nuclei

8 Node of Ranvier

FIG. 4. — *Nerve (sciatic), longitudinal section.*
Stain: Protargol and aniline blue. 800×.

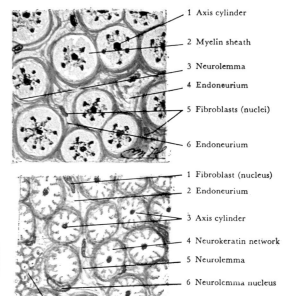

1 Axis cylinder

2 Myelin sheath

3 Neurolemma

4 Endoneurium

5 Fibroblasts (nuclei)

6 Endoneurium

1 Fibroblast (nucleus)

2 Endoneurium

3 Axis cylinder

4 Neurokeratin network

5 Neurolemma

6 Neurolemma nucleus

7 Endoneurium

8 Small myelinated nerve fibers

FIG. 5. (above) — *Nerve, as in Fig. 4, transverse section.*
FIG. 6. (below) — *Nerve (branch of the vagus), transverse section.*
Stain: Mallory-Azan. 800×.

PLATE 30

FIG. 1. DORSAL ROOT GANGLION: PANORAMIC VIEW
(LONGITUDINAL SECTION)

A layer of connective tissue, rich in adipose cells and containing many blood vessels, surrounds the mass of nervous tissue (1, 6, 14). It merges with the external capsule of the ganglion, the epineurium (2), which is continuous with the epineurium of the dorsal root (3) and with that of the peripheral nerve (11). Larger perineurial septa may be seen (4) but neither perineurium nor endoneurium are distinguishable at this magnification.

Large numbers of rounded unipolar ganglion cells make up the bulk of the ganglion (9), and are conspicuous because of their size and staining capacity. Their vesicular nuclei with nucleoli are visible but will be seen better at a higher magnification (Fig. 2). Bundles of nerve fibers may be seen between groups of ganglion cells. The larger bundles tend to run in a longitudinal direction (10) and will either enter the dorsal root (5) or the peripheral nerve (12). These nerve fibers represent, respectively, the central processes and peripheral processes formed by the bifurcation of the single axonal process which emerges from each ganglion cell.

The ventral root (8) joins the nerve fibers emerging from the ganglion (13) to form the peripheral nerve.

FIG. 2. SECTION OF A DORSAL ROOT GANGLION

At a higher magnification, one sees ganglion cells of various sizes. The characteristic vesicular nucleus with its prominent nucleolus (2) is conspicuous. The cytoplasm is filled with fine Nissl bodies (3). Some cells display a small clump of lipochrome pigment (5). Each cell has an axon hillock (not illustrated).

Within the perineuronal space, in intimate relationship with the ganglion cells, are satellite cells with rounded or oval nuclei, of neuroectodermal origin, forming a loose inner layer of the capsule (6). An outer capsule of more flattened fibroblasts and fibers (7) is continuous with the endoneurium. In sections, these two layers are not always clearly distinguishable; often the two cell types appear to be intermingled, as around the cell with the lipochrome pigment (5).

Between ganglion cells are seen many fibroblasts (4), randomly arranged in the connective tissue framework, or in rows in the endoneurium between nerve fibers (8 right, 1). With hematoxylin-eosin, small nerve fibers and connective tissue are not differentiated. Larger myelinated fibers are recognizable when sectioned longitudinally (1).

FIG. 3. SECTION OF A SYMPATHETIC TRUNK GANGLION

Like the dorsal root ganglion cells, sympathetic trunk ganglion cells have the characteristic nucleus and nucleolus (sometimes more than one nucleolus) and small Nissl bodies throughout the cytoplasm.

They are small multipolar cells, therefore cell outlines are often irregular and stumps of processes may be present (6). Nuclei are often eccentrically placed (6); binucleated cells are common. Most cells contain lipochrome pigment.

Satellite cells are usually less numerous than in dorsal root ganglion cells (2, 5). The connective tissue capsule may or may not be well defined (3).

In the intercellular areas (4) are fibroblasts, supporting connective tissue, blood vessels, unmyelinated and thinly-myelinated fibers. Nerve fibers aggregate into bundles (1, 7) which course through the sympathetic trunk; they represent preganglionic fibers, postganglionic visceral efferent fibers and visceral afferent fibers.

PLATE 30

NERVOUS TISSUE: GANGLIA

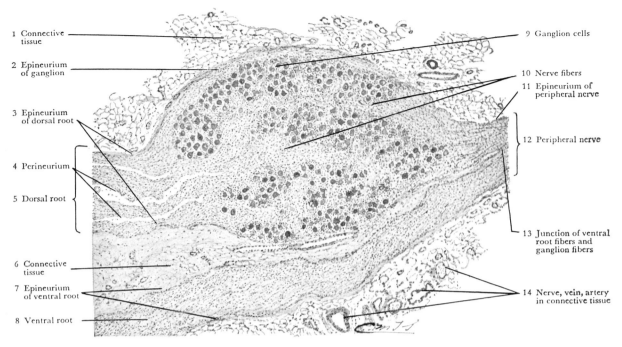

1 Connective tissue

2 Epineurium of ganglion

3 Epineurium of dorsal root

4 Perineurium

5 Dorsal root

6 Connective tissue

7 Epineurium of ventral root

8 Ventral root

9 Ganglion cells

10 Nerve fibers

11 Epineurium of peripheral nerve

12 Peripheral nerve

13 Junction of ventral root fibers and ganglion fibers

14 Nerve, vein, artery in connective tissue

FIG. 1. — *Dorsal root ganglion: panoramic view (longitudinal section).*
Stain: hematoxylin-eosin. 25×.

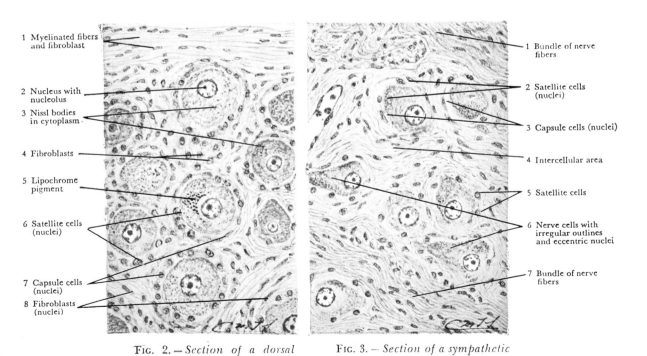

1 Myelinated fibers and fibroblast

2 Nucleus with nucleolus

3 Nissl bodies in cytoplasm

4 Fibroblasts

5 Lipochrome pigment

6 Satellite cells (nuclei)

7 Capsule cells (nuclei)

8 Fibroblasts (nuclei)

1 Bundle of nerve fibers

2 Satellite cells (nuclei)

3 Capsule cells (nuclei)

4 Intercellular area

5 Satellite cells

6 Nerve cells with irregular outlines and eccentric nuclei

7 Bundle of nerve fibers

FIG. 2. — *Section of a dorsal root ganglion.*
Stain: hematoxylin-eosin. 400×.

FIG. 3. — *Section of a sympathetic trunk ganglion.*
Stain: hematoxylin-eosin. 400×.

PLATE 31 (Fig. 1)

SPINAL CORD: CERVICAL REGION (PANORAMIC VIEW, TRANSVERSE SECTION)

In a transverse section through fresh tissue of a spinal cord, the substance of the cord is seen to be divided into outer white matter and inner gray matter. In stained material, the two areas are readily seen but, of course, lose the significance of the terms "white" and "gray."

The inner gray matter has the shape of an H. The crossbar is known as the gray commissure (16). The anterior (ventral) horn or column (17) is thicker and shorter than the posterior (dorsal) horn or column (14). In the anterior (ventral) horn lie two groups of nerve cell bodies: neuromotor cells of the anteromedial column (8) and neuromotor cells of the anterolateral column (7). Unmyelinated fibers (17) are clearly seen in this area. Certain of these fibers (9) penetrate the white matter to the periphery of the cord, at which point they will emerge obliquely as components of the anterior (ventral) roots (20). The posterior (dorsal) horn has only isolated nerve cell bodies (5).

The spinal cord on the posterior (dorsal) surface bears a longitudinal shallow groove in the midline, the posterior median sulcus (10). A neuroglial membrane, the posterior (dorsal) median septum (13), extends inward from the sulcus dividing the white matter in the posterior area into right and left halves. Each half in turn is divided by a less conspicuous postero-intermediate septum (12) into a postero-medial column, the fasciculus gracilis (Goll's column) (11) and a postero-lateral column, the fasciculus cuneatus (Burdach's column) (1).

A transverse section of the ependymal canal is seen in the middle of the gray commissure (15). Above and below the canal, the gray matter is referred to as the dorsal and ventral gray commissure respectively. A ventral white commissure is usually seen below the ventral gray one.

The most peripheral part of the spinal cord is the marginal (superficial) glial membrane (4), an area free of nerve fibers. Pia mater is indicated by a yellow zone around the cord; it is seen best in the anterior ventral fissure (19).

PLATE 31 (Fig. 2)

SPINAL CORD: NERVE CELLS OF THE ANTERIOR (VENTRAL) HORN (SECTIONAL VIEW)

Nerve cell bodies (10) and processes (2) of the motor neurons in the anterior (ventral) horn are shown here under higher magnification. The nucleus possesses a prominent nucleolus (7), although in those cells which have been sectioned tangentially, not even the nucleus appears clearly (8). Neurofibrils lie in the cytoplasm of the nerve cell bodies and continue into the processes. Cut fibers (9) appear in the areas between the nerve cell bodies. Other cells (6) are neuroglia.

The white matter is composed of nerve cell fibers cut longitudinally (4) or transversely (5). Transverse sections show the central axis cylinder (3) or axon, which appears as a brown dot, surrounded by a clear circular space, which is occupied by the myelin sheath in fresh tissue.

PLATE 31

SPINAL CORD: CERVICAL REGION
(TRANSVERSE SECTION)

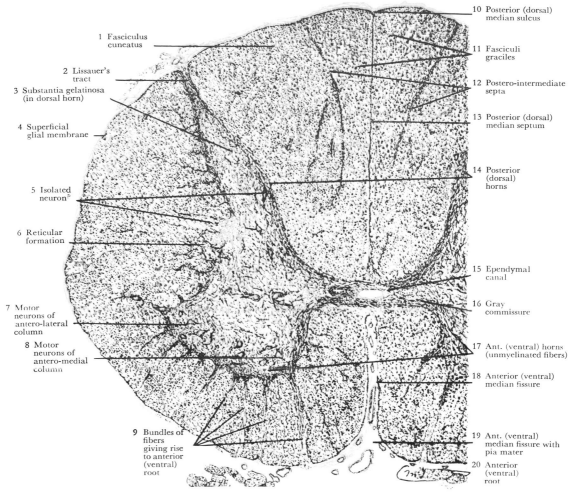

1 Fasciculus cuneatus

2 Lissauer's tract

3 Substantia gelatinosa (in dorsal horn)

4 Superficial glial membrane

5 Isolated neuron

6 Reticular formation

7 Motor neurons of antero-lateral column

8 Motor neurons of antero-medial column

9 Bundles of fibers giving rise to anterior (ventral) root

10 Posterior (dorsal) median sulcus

11 Fasciculi graciles

12 Postero-intermediate septa

13 Posterior (dorsal) median septum

14 Posterior (dorsal) horns

15 Ependymal canal

16 Gray commissure

17 Ant. (ventral) horns (unmyelinated fibers)

18 Anterior (ventral) median fissure

19 Ant. (ventral) median fissure with pia mater

20 Anterior (ventral) root

FIG. 1. — *Cervical region (panoramic view).*
Silver impregnation: Cajal's method. 18×.

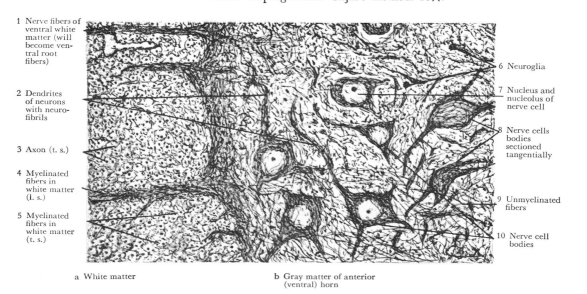

1 Nerve fibers of ventral white matter (will become ventral root fibers)

2 Dendrites of neurons with neurofibrils

3 Axon (t. s.)

4 Myelinated fibers in white matter (l. s.)

5 Myelinated fibers in white matter (t. s.)

6 Neuroglia

7 Nucleus and nucleolus of nerve cell

8 Nerve cells bodies sectioned tangentially

9 Unmyelinated fibers

10 Nerve cell bodies

a White matter

b Gray matter of anterior (ventral) horn

FIG. 2. — *Nerve cells of the anterior (ventral) horn and adjacent white matter.*
Silver impregnation: Cajal's method. 160×.

PLATE 32 (Fig. 1)

SPINAL CORD: MID-THORACIC REGION
(TRANSVERSE SECTION, PANORAMIC VIEW)

This illustration represents a transverse section of mid-thoracic cord, as seen in a routine hematoxylin-eosin preparation. It differs in several ways from the section of cervical cord represented in Plate 31. The dorsal gray columns (posterior or dorsal horns) are slender (5). At their ventromedial basal portion one sees the nucleus dorsalis (column of Clarke), a prominent structure because of the number and size of its neuron cell bodies (22). The lateral gray columns are well developed, and contain the small-celled lateral sympathetic nucleus (23). The ventral gray columns (anterior horns) are small, the number of motor cells is reduced to only a few cells in both the medial and lateral motor nuclei (24).

Other structures in this section of mid-thoracic cord are seen in corresponding areas of the cervical cord in Plate 31, differing only in appearance because of the stain used.

Shown here, in addition, are the meninges of the spinal cord. The fibrous pia mater (9), innermost layer of the meninges, adheres closely to the superficial (marginal) glial membrane of the cord, which is seen here indistinctly. In the pia mater are small blood vessels, as well as larger ones (1, 15), which supply the cord. Fine trabeculae in the subarachnoid space (10) connect the pia mater with the arachnoid (11); this space is normally filled with cerebrospinal fluid. Externally, there is a thick, fibrous dura mater (13), separated from the arachnoid by the subdural space (12). In this preparation, the subdural space is unusually large because of artificial retraction of the arachnoid.

PLATE 32 (Fig. 2)

NERVE CELLS OF SOME TYPICAL REGIONS OF THE CORD

Nerve cells, situated in the gray matter, present different characteristics according to the region they occupy and the function they carry out.

In this plate are shown several anterior horn cells (a), whose characteristics have been described in Plate 25, Fig. 1. Only the staining reaction is different here. The typical vesicular nucleus, with its prominent nucleolus, is centrally located. When the section passes through the superficial portion of a cell, the nucleus is not seen (2). Nissl substance appears as large clumps (1), uniformly distributed throughout the cytoplasm, and extends partway into the dendrites (4). The clear axon hillock and the beginning of the axon may be seen in some cells (3). These axons contribute to the formation of the ventral roots and terminate by innervating skeletal muscle (motor nerves).

The two cells in (b) are posterior horn cells from the substantia gelatinosa. They are much smaller than anterior horn cells, are ovoid or polygonal in shape, Nissl granules are fine, and the nucleus is usually deeply-stained. They are considered as association cells, especially for incoming pain and temperature impulses.

At (c) are represented two cells of the lateral sympathetic nucleus, located in the lateral gray column. These are also small cells, somewhat larger than those of the substantia gelatinosa, but show similar features. Their axons enter the ventral roots, and pass by way of white rami to vertebral or prevertebral ganglia.

The final group (d) represents cells from the nucleus dorsalis (column of Clarke); its location is seen at (22) in Fig. 1. They are large multipolar cells, similar in size to anterior horn cells. Nissl substance is in the form of clumps, which are characteristically situated at the periphery of the cell (5). The typical vesicular nucleus with its nucleolus is eccentrically placed (7). As usual, the nucleus is not seen when the section passes through the periphery of the cell (6). These cells receive incoming proprioceptive fibers.

PLATE 32

SPINAL CORD. MID-THORACIC REGION (TRANSVERSE SECTION)

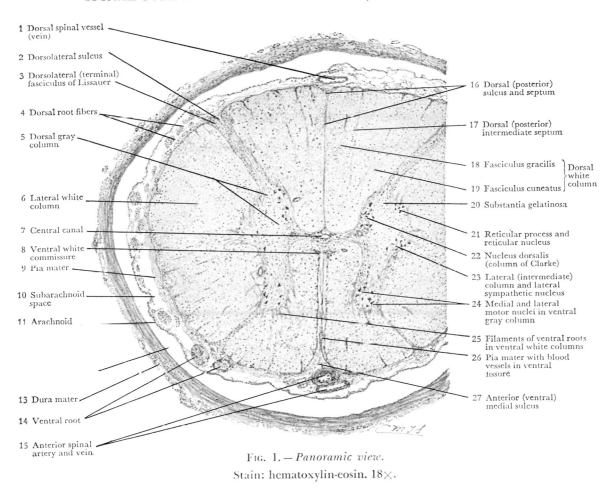

1 Dorsal spinal vessel (vein)

2 Dorsolateral sulcus

3 Dorsolateral (terminal) fasciculus of Lissauer

4 Dorsal root fibers

5 Dorsal gray column

6 Lateral white column

7 Central canal

8 Ventral white commissure

9 Pia mater

10 Subarachnoid space

11 Arachnoid

13 Dura mater

14 Ventral root

15 Anterior spinal artery and vein

16 Dorsal (posterior) sulcus and septum

17 Dorsal (posterior) intermediate septum

18 Fasciculus gracilis ⎫ Dorsal white column
19 Fasciculus cuneatus ⎭

20 Substantia gelatinosa

21 Reticular process and reticular nucleus

22 Nucleus dorsalis (column of Clarke)

23 Lateral (intermediate) column and lateral sympathetic nucleus

24 Medial and lateral motor nuclei in ventral gray column

25 Filaments of ventral roots in ventral white columns

26 Pia mater with blood vessels in ventral fissure

27 Anterior (ventral) medial sulcus

Fig. 1. — *Panoramic view.*
Stain: hematoxylin-eosin. 18×.

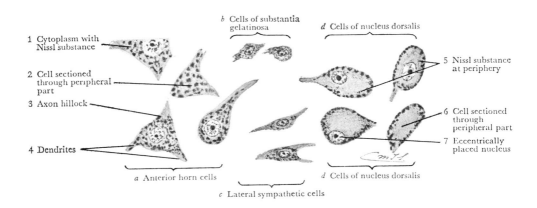

b Cells of substantia gelatinosa

d Cells of nucleus dorsalis

1 Cytoplasm with Nissl substance

2 Cell sectioned through peripheral part

3 Axon hillock

4 Dendrites

5 Nissl substance at periphery

6 Cell sectioned through peripheral part

7 Eccentrically placed nucleus

a Anterior horn cells

c Lateral sympathetic cells

d Cells of nucleus dorsalis

Fig. 2. — *Nerve cells of some typical regions of the spinal cord.*
Stain: hematoxylin-eosin. 380×.

Plate 33 (Fig. 1)

CEREBELLUM (SECTIONAL VIEW, TRANSVERSE SECTION)

The cerebellum is composed of inner white matter (4) and outer gray matter (3).

The white matter (4) has a uniform aspect and is made up of myelinated fibers; its ramifications (10) form the core of the numerous cerebellar folds.

The gray matter constitutes the cortex. Three layers can be distinguished in the cortex: an outer molecular layer (6), with relatively few cells and with fibers directed horizontally; an inner granular layer (7) with numerous small cells with intensely stained nuclei; and an intermediate layer of Purkinje cells (8). The cells of Purkinje are pyriform and have an abundance of ramified dendrites which extend into the molecular layer.

Plate 33 (Fig. 2)

CEREBELLUM: CORTEX

The most conspicuous entities forming the intermediate layer are the Purkinje cells (8), with their ramifications upward into the granular layer of the cerebellum. Surrounding the Purkinje cells are nerve fibers (4), which form the so-called baskets of the stellate cells (7) of the molecular layer.

In the molecular layer at the top of the illustration, the following structures are shown: the cell bodies of the stellate cells (7), directed horizontally; the thick granular dendrites of the Purkinje cells (3); the processes of the stellate cells (4), well stained but finer and more homogenous than the former; and axon processes (2) which extend into the molecular layer from cells of the granular layer.

In the granular layer at the bottom of the illustration, the following structures are shown; the granular cells of the cerebellum (5), which are small and numerous; stellate cells (6), which are larger and have more abundant cytoplasm, and "clear" areas called glomeruli or islands (10) in which nerve cells are sparse or absent, where synaptic connections occur.

PLATE 33

CEREBELLUM

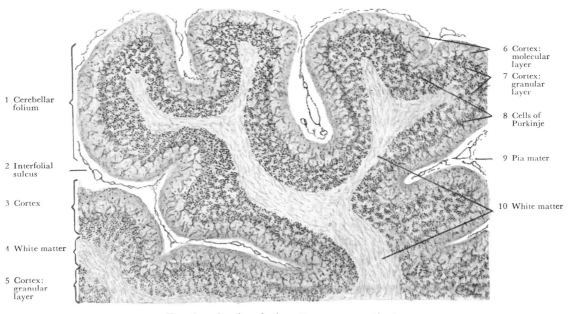

1 Cerebellar folium

2 Interfolial sulcus

3 Cortex

4 White matter

5 Cortex: granular layer

6 Cortex: molecular layer

7 Cortex: granular layer

8 Cells of Purkinje

9 Pia mater

10 White matter

FIG. 1. — *Sectional view (transverse section)*.
Silver impregnation: Cajal's method. 45×.

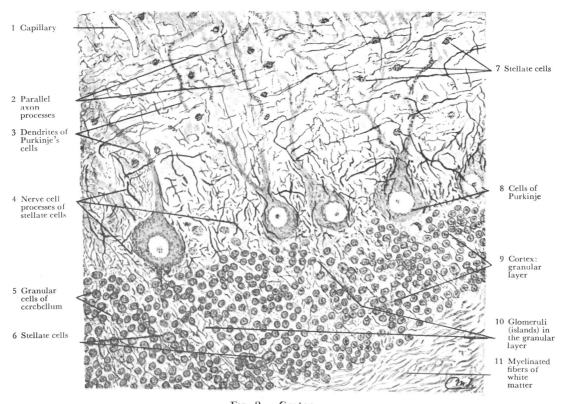

1 Capillary

2 Parallel axon processes

3 Dendrites of Purkinje's cells

4 Nerve cell processes of stellate cells

5 Granular cells of cerebellum

6 Stellate cells

7 Stellate cells

8 Cells of Purkinje

9 Cortex: granular layer

10 Glomeruli (islands) in the granular layer

11 Myelinated fibers of white matter

FIG. 2. — *Cortex*.
Silver impregnation: Cajal's method. 300×.

PLATE 34 (Fig. 1)

CEREBRAL CORTEX: SECTION PERPENDICULAR TO THE SURFACE OF THE CORTEX

Considerable variation occurs in the nomenclature of layers of the cortex. This is largely because the layers are not uniform throughout the cortex. In the accompanying figure they are labelled as listed on the left.

The outermost layer of cerebral tissue is the plexiform layer (1). Its peripheral portion is composed exclusively of horizontally directed nerve cell fibers. In its deeper part lie Cajal's horizontal cells (10), which are stellate- or spindle-shaped and give rise to the above-mentioned processes. Overlying the plexiform layer is the fine network of connective tissue, the pia mater (8).

Farther down in the cortical substance lie the characteristic pyramidal cells (11, 13) of the cortex. Those situated nearer the surface (11) are smaller than those more deeply placed (13). The ascending process from each of these cells is a dendrite.

In the inner granular layer (4), polymorphous cells (12) are present in addition to the pyramidal cells.

In the deep layers of the cortex (6) the polymorphous cells predominate (15); pyramidal cells are lacking. Axons from the former are relatively short and penetrate into the white substance of the brain.

Beneath the layer of polymorphous cells are the myelinated fibers (16) of the white matter of the brain.

PLATE 34 (Fig. 2)

CEREBRAL CORTEX: CENTRAL AREA OF THE CORTEX

Under a higher magnification, the pyramidal cells (1, 6) are seen to have numerous neurofibrils in the cytoplasm; the nucleus (3) is vesicular with relatively little dispersed chromatin and an eccentrically placed nucleolus. The outstanding nerve cell process is the main dendrite, which extends upward toward the surface of the brain, occasionally with branches.

There is an abundance of nerve fibers (2) among the nerve cells. Only a few neuroglial cells (4) are in evidence.

PLATE 34

CEREBRAL CORTEX

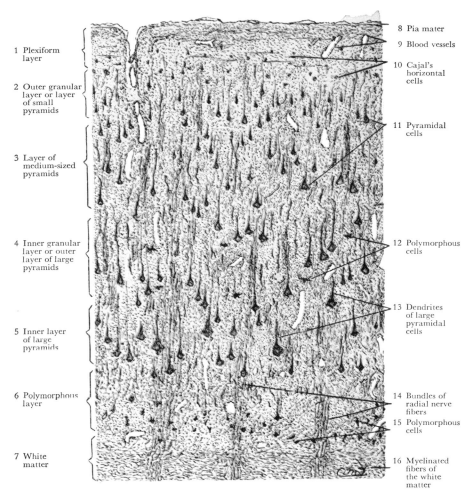

1 Plexiform layer

2 Outer granular layer or layer of small pyramids

3 Layer of medium-sized pyramids

4 Inner granular layer or outer layer of large pyramids

5 Inner layer of large pyramids

6 Polymorphous layer

7 White matter

8 Pia mater

9 Blood vessels

10 Cajal's horizontal cells

11 Pyramidal cells

12 Polymorphous cells

13 Dendrites of large pyramidal cells

14 Bundles of radial nerve fibers

15 Polymorphous cells

16 Myelinated fibers of the white matter

FIG. 1. — *Section perpendicular to the cortical surface.*
Reduced silver nitrate method of Cajal. 80×.

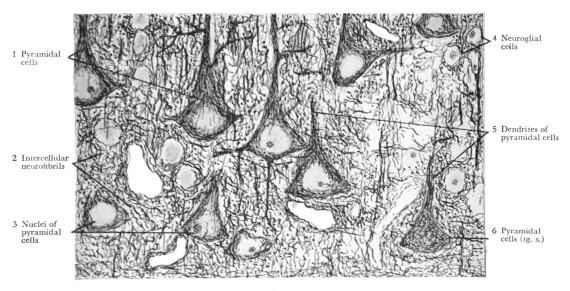

1 Pyramidal cells

2 Intercellular neurofibrils

3 Nuclei of pyramidal cells

4 Neuroglial cells

5 Dendrites of pyramidal cells

6 Pyramidal cells (tg. s.)

FIG. 2. — *Central area of the cortex.*
Reduced silver nitrate method of Cajal. 300×.

PLATE 35 (Fig. 1)

BLOOD AND LYMPH VESSELS (TRANSVERSE SECTION)

This plate illustrates various types of blood vessels and a lymph vessel, surrounded by loose connective tissue and numerous adipose cells (13, 27).

An artery of small size, a muscular artery, is shown at the top center of the plate. It illustrates the basic structure of an artery. In contrast to a vein, an artery has a relatively thick wall and small lumen. The artery shows the following constituent layers:

a. Tunica intima, composed of the inner endothelium (16), a sub-endothelial layer of connective tissue (17), and an elastica interna (19).

b. Tunica media (4), composed predominantly of circular smooth muscle fibers. Fine elastic fibers are interspersed.

c. Tunica adventitia (6), composed of connective tissue in which lie nerve fibers (14) and blood vessels (15). The latter are collectively called the vasa vasorum (15), or "blood vessels of blood vessels."

When muscular arteries acquire about 25 or more layers of smooth muscle in the tunica media, they are referred to as medium-sized arteries. Elastic fibers become more numerous, but are still present as thin fibers and networks.

A medium-sized vein is shown at the lower center of the plate. It has a relatively thin wall and large lumen, the latter containing coagulated blood. The vein shows the following constituent layers:

a. Tunica intima, composed in this case of only the endothelium (23). Sometimes the tunica intima of a vein also has a thin layer of fine collagenous and elastic fibers.

b. Tunica media (24), consisting of a thin layer of circular smooth muscle fibers.

c. Tunica adventitia (25), consisting of a wide layer of connective tissue.

A lymphatic vessel (12) can be recognized by the thinness of its wall and the flaps of a valve in the lumen. Many veins have similar valves.

Arterioles are illustrated (1, 5, 8, 21). The smallest arteriole (1) has a thin elastic membrane and a single layer of muscle in the media. One is sectioned longitudinally (8). Venules (3, 26), capillaries (11, 20) and nerves (2, 22), are in evidence.

PLATE 35 (Fig. 2)

LARGE VEIN: PORTAL VEIN (TRANSVERSE SECTION)

In large veins, the outstanding feature is the thick, muscular adventitia, with its smooth muscle fibers oriented longitudinally. In this transverse section of the portal vein, the typical arrangement is noted: the muscle is in bundles, here seen mainly in cross sections (1), with varying amounts of connective tissue dispersed between them (2). Vasa vasorum (3, 7) are present in this intervening connective tissue.

In contrast, the media is a thinner layer of circularly arranged muscle (6), somewhat loosely arranged in connective tissue in this portal vein; in other large veins it may be a very thin, more compact layer. As in other vessels, the intima is of endothelium (4) supported by a small amount of connective tissue. In addition, large veins usually demonstrate an internal elastic membrane (5).

PLATE 35

FIG. 1. BLOOD AND LYMPH VESSELS (TRANSVERSE SECTION)

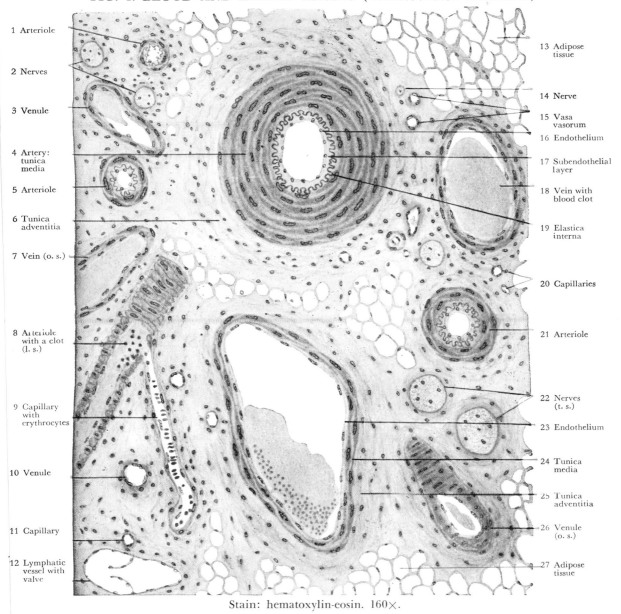

1 Arteriole

2 Nerves

3 Venule

4 Artery: tunica media

5 Arteriole

6 Tunica adventitia

7 Vein (o. s.)

8 Arteriole with a clot (l. s.)

9 Capillary with erythrocytes

10 Venule

11 Capillary

12 Lymphatic vessel with valve

13 Adipose tissue

14 Nerve

15 Vasa vasorum

16 Endothelium

17 Subendothelial layer

18 Vein with blood clot

19 Elastica interna

20 Capillaries

21 Arteriole

22 Nerves (t. s.)

23 Endothelium

24 Tunica media

25 Tunica adventitia

26 Venule (o. s.)

27 Adipose tissue

Stain: hematoxylin-eosin. 160×.

FIG. 2. LARGE VEIN: PORTAL VEIN (TRANSVERSE SECTION)

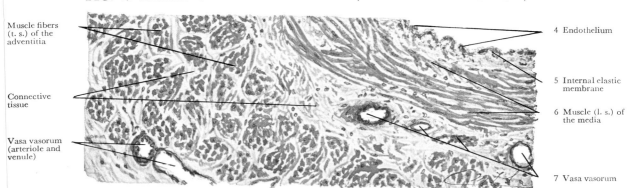

Muscle fibers (t. s.) of the adventitia

Connective tissue

Vasa vasorum (arteriole and venule)

4 Endothelium

5 Internal elastic membrane

6 Muscle (l. s.) of the media

7 Vasa vasorum

Stain: hematoxylin-eosin. 200×.

PLATE 37

HEART: LEFT ATRIUM AND VENTRICLE (PANORAMIC VIEW, LONGITUDINAL SECTION)

The plate represents a longitudinal section of the left heart showing the atrium, the atrioventricular (mitral) valve, and the ventricle.

In the atrium are seen the endocardium (1) consisting of endothelium and a thick subendothelial connective tissue, the myocardium (2) with the musculature arranged rather loosely, the epicardium (13), of mesothelium and a very thin layer of connective tissue, and the subepicardial connective tissue and fat (14) which varies in amount in different regions. This layer extends also into the atrioventricular groove and into the ventricle.

In the ventricle, the endocardium (6) is thin in comparison with that in the atrium, and the myocardium (7) is thick and more compact. The cardiac musculature is seen in various planes of section. The epicardium and subepicardial connective tissue (16) are continuous with those in the atrium.

Between the atrium and ventricle is seen the annulus fibrosus (3) of dense fibrous connective tissue, and a leaflet of the atrioventricular (mitral) valve (4), formed by a double membrane of endocardium (4a) and a core of dense connective tissue (4b) continuous with the annulus fibrosus. At (5) is shown the insertion of a chorda tendina into the valve.

On the inner surface of the ventricular wall, one can distinguish the characteristic prominences of the myocardium and endocardium: the apex of a papillary muscle (18) and two columnae carneae above this (17).

Purkinje fibers, located in the loose subendocardial tissue, may be distinguished by their larger size and lighter staining (8). The small area within the rectangle (10) is shown at a higher magnification in Plate 38, Fig. 2.

The larger coronary vessels course in the subepicardial connective tissue. An artery is seen at (10). Below it is a section of the coronary sinus (11), and entering it, a coronary vein and its valve (12). Smaller coronary vessels may be seen in the subepicardial connective and in the many perimysial septa extending into the myocardium (15).

PLATE 37

HEART: LEFT ATRIUM AND VENTRICLE
(PANORAMIC VIEW, LONGITUDINAL SECTION)

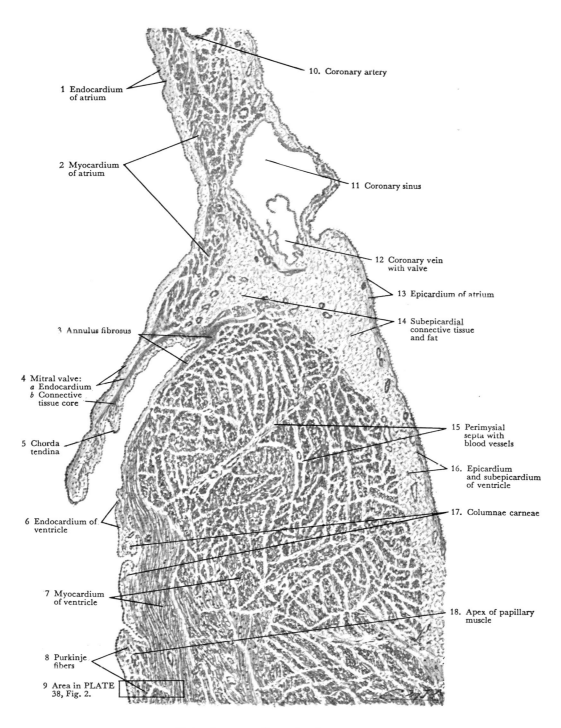

1 Endocardium of atrium

2 Myocardium of atrium

3 Annulus fibrosus

4 Mitral valve:
a Endocardium
b Connective tissue core

5 Chorda tendina

6 Endocardium of ventricle

7 Myocardium of ventricle

8 Purkinje fibers

9 Area in PLATE 38, Fig. 2.

10. Coronary artery

11 Coronary sinus

12 Coronary vein with valve

13 Epicardium of atrium

14 Subepicardial connective tissue and fat

15 Perimysial septa with blood vessels

16. Epicardium and subepicardium of ventricle

17. Columnae carneae

18. Apex of papillary muscle

Stain: hematoxylin-eosin. 6×.

PLATE 38 (Fig. 1)

HEART: PULMONARY ARTERY, PULMONARY VALVE, RIGHT VENTRICLE (PANORAMIC VIEW, LONGITUDINAL SECTION)

A portion of the right ventricle, from which the pulmonary artery leaves, is represented in this plate.

A section of the wall of the pulmonary artery is seen at (6). The endothelium of its intima is distinguishable on its right surface. The media makes up the largest part of its wall; its thick elastic lamellae are not apparent at this magnification. A thin adventitia merges into the surrounding subepicardial connective tissue (2), which contains large amounts of fat in this specimen.

The pulmonary artery arises at (8) from the annulus fibrosus (9). One leaflet of the pulmonary (semilunar) valve is seen at (7). Like the mitral valve, it is covered with endocardium, and connective tissue from the annulus fibrosus extends into its base (10) and forms a central core.

The thick myocardium (4) of the right ventricle is covered on its internal surface by endocardium (11). The endocardium continues without interruption over the pulmonary valve and the annulus fibrosus, and becomes continuous with the intima of the pulmonary artery (in the region of 8).

The external surface of the pulmonary artery is covered with subepicardial connective tissue and fat (2), and this in turn is covered with epicardium (1). Both of these layers pass uninterruptedly over the external wall of the ventricle. Coronary vessels are seen in the subepicardium (3, 5).

PLATE 38 (Fig. 2)

PURKINJE FIBERS (HEMATOXYLIN-EOSIN)

The area outlined by the rectangle (10) in Plate 37, is represented here at a high magnification (400×). Below the endocardium (1) are seen groups of Purkinje fibers, which are differentiated from typical cardiac muscle fibers (5) because of their larger size and their less intense staining. Some of the Purkinje fibers are sectioned transversely (2), others in longitudinal section (4). In the transverse sections, it is seen clearly that Purkinje fibers have fewer myofibrils, and that these are arranged peripherally, leaving a perinuclear zone of comparatively clear sarcoplasm. A nucleus is seen in some of the transverse sections; in others, a central area of sarcoplasm is seen, the section having passed above or below the nucleus.

Purkinje fibers merge with cardiac fibers. At (3) is seen a transitional fiber; the upper part corresponds to a Purkinje fiber, the lower part to an ordinary cardiac fiber.

PLATE 38 (Fig. 3)

PURKINJE FIBERS (MALLORY-AZAN)

This figure is reproduced from a cardiac area where Purkinje fibers were abundant, in a preparation stained with Mallory-Azan, at the same high magnification as in Fig. 2.

The characteristic features of Purkinje fibers are well demonstrated in longitudinal and transverse sections (2).

With hematoxylin-eosin, connective tissue is not too apparent. In this preparation, blue staining of collagenous fibers shows conspicuously the subendocardial connective tissue (3) surrounding the Purkinje fibers. A capillary with red blood corpuscles is seen (1).

PLATE 38

FIG. 1. HEART:
PULMONARY ARTERY, PULMONARY VALVE, RIGHT
VENTRICLE (PANORAMIC VIEW, LONGITUDINAL SECTION)

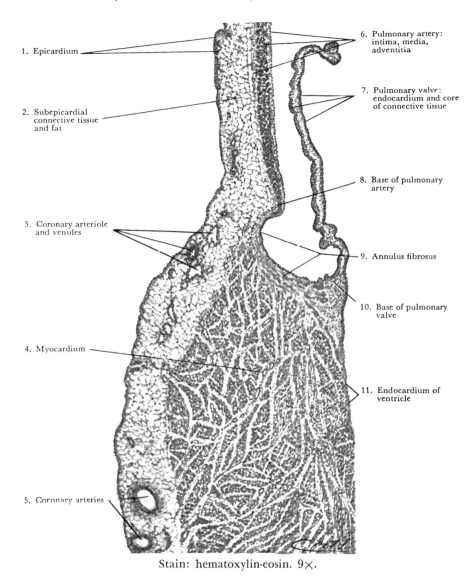

1. Epicardium

2. Subepicardial connective tissue and fat

3. Coronary arteriole and venules

4. Myocardium

5. Coronary arteries

6. Pulmonary artery: intima, media, adventitia

7. Pulmonary valve: endocardium and core of connective tissue

8. Base of pulmonary artery

9. Annulus fibrosus

10. Base of pulmonary valve

11. Endocardium of ventricle

Stain: hematoxylin-eosin. 9×.

FIGS. 2 and 3: PURKINJE FIBERS

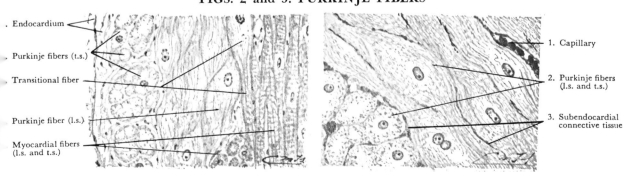

. Endocardium

Purkinje fibers (t.s.)

Transitional fiber

Purkinje fiber (l.s.)

Myocardial fibers (l.s. and t.s.)

1. Capillary

2. Purkinje fibers (l.s. and t.s.)

3. Subendocardial connective tissue

Fig. 2. Stain: hematoxylin-eosin. 400×.   Fig. 3. Stain: Mallory-Azan. 400×.

PLATE 39

LYMPH NODE (PANORAMIC VIEW)

A lymph node is composed of a mass of lymphocytes and lymphoblasts intermeshed with sinuses and encased by a capsule of connective tissue (2). In the cortex (3) of the node, the lymph cells form nodules (13). In many of the nodules the center is lightly stained; these are the germinal centers (15). In the medulla (4) of the node, the lymph cells form cords (12). The medullary (11) and trabecular sinuses surround these formations. Immediately under the capsule (2) lies the cortical or subcapsular sinus (14).

Trabeculae of connective tissue (5), lying between the nodules of the cortex, extend inward from the capsule (2). In the medulla these trabeculae ramify and anastomose around the medullary cords and in the sinuses.

The capsule is surrounded by loose connective tissue in which there are blood vessels (8, 16) and adipose cells (7).

At the upper right of the lymph node is the hilus (10). At the hilus lie the efferent lymphatic vessels (9), which drain lymph from the node. Veins and arteries supplying the node also pierce the capsule at the hilus.

PLATE 39

LYMPH NODE (PANORAMIC VIEW)

1 Lymphatic
parenchyma

2 Capsule

3 Cortex

4 Medulla

5 Trabeculae
of connective
tissue

6 Blood
vessels

7 Adipose
tissue

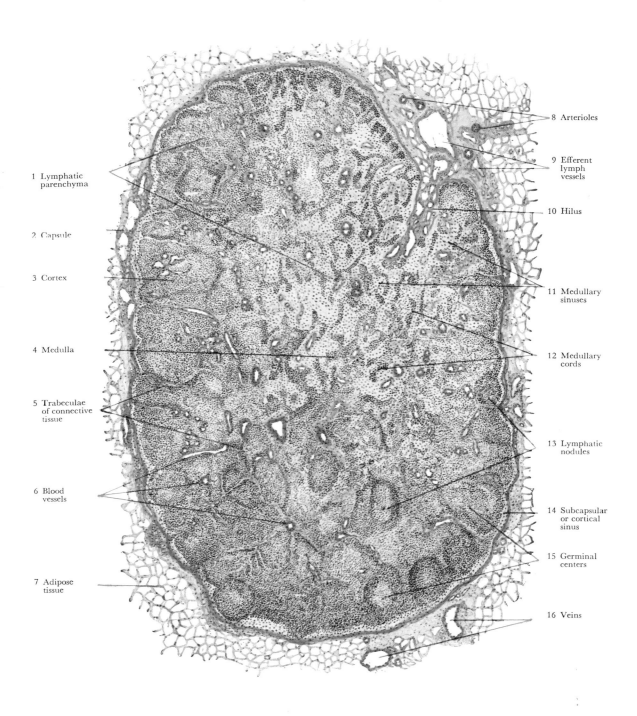

8 Arterioles

9 Efferent
lymph
vessels

10 Hilus

11 Medullary
sinuses

12 Medullary
cords

13 Lymphatic
nodules

14 Subcapsular
or cortical
sinus

15 Germinal
centers

16 Veins

Stain: hematoxylin-eosin. 32×.

PLATE 40

LYMPH NODE (SECTIONAL VIEW)

Part of Plate 39 is shown here under a higher magnification, illustrating the relationship between a single cortical nodule and the capsule and medulla.

The capsule is surrounded by loose connective tissue (1), containing blood vessels (2, 3, 4) and lymph vessels (13); the latter have a thin endothelial lining and valves (14). From the capsule (5), trabeculae of fibrous connective tissue (15) extend to the medulla. Blood vessels accompany these partitions into the substance of the node.

Reticular connective tissue forms the stroma of the nodules and cords and of the subcapsular sinus (6), trabecular sinus (16), and medullary sinuses (12, 19). Relatively few lymph cells occur in the sinuses. However, in the nodules of the cortex (7) and the medullary cords (11, 18), lymph cells are in such abundance as to hide the reticulum unless special staining methods are used. Most of the lymph cells are small lymphocytes, with large nuclei containing dense accumulation of chromatin and very little cytoplasm. They appear as deeply stained violet dots. The central part of the nodule stains less deeply; this is the germinal center (8). In the germinal center, cells are less numerous and have more cytoplasm; here the larger cells are lymphoblasts and most of the smaller are medium-sized lymphocytes.

PLATE 40

LYMPH NODE (SECTIONAL VIEW)

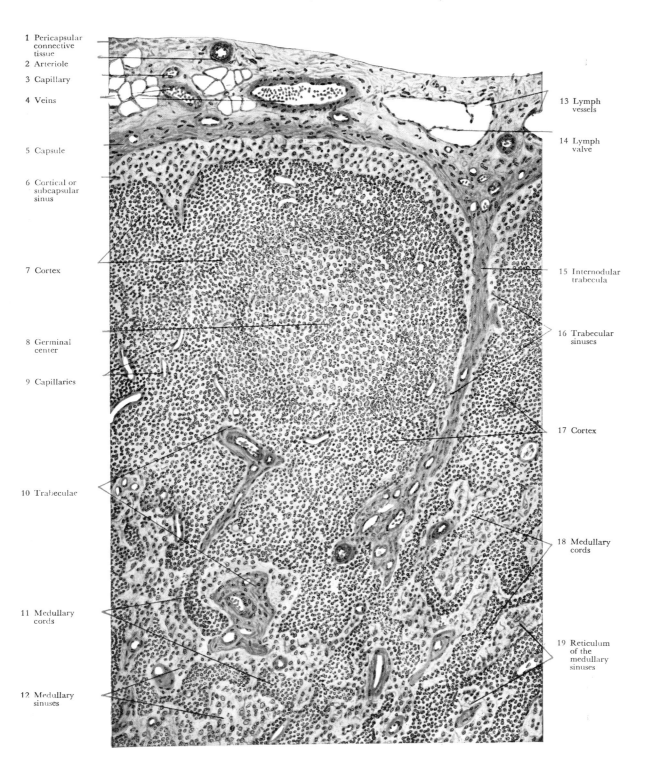

1 Pericapsular connective tissue
2 Arteriole
3 Capillary
4 Veins
5 Capsule
6 Cortical or subcapsular sinus
7 Cortex
8 Germinal center
9 Capillaries
10 Trabeculae
11 Medullary cords
12 Medullary sinuses

13 Lymph vessels
14 Lymph valve
15 Internodular trabecula
16 Trabecular sinuses
17 Cortex
18 Medullary cords
19 Reticulum of the medullary sinuses

Stain: hematoxylin-eosin. 150×.

PLATE 41 (Fig. 1).   **SPLEEN (PANORAMIC VIEW)**

From the capsule (1), trabeculae (3) of connective tissue extend into the body of the spleen. In transverse sections, such trabeculae may look like nodules of connective tissue (11). Trabeculae extending inward from the hilum carry the trabecular arteries (3a) and trabecular veins (10).

Throughout the spleen are lymphatic nodules, the splenic corpuscles (2, 7), or Malpighian corpuscles (older terminology). In young individuals, they contain germinal centers (6). Through each splenic corpuscle passes an arteriole, the central artery (5, 8), which is usually eccentrically placed within the corpuscle.

Surrounding the lymphatic nodules and intermeshed with the trabeculae is a diffuse mass of cells which collectively forms the red pulp, because it appears as a reddish paste in fresh tissue. This mass contains the venous sinuses (9) of the splenic cords (cords of Billroth) (4). The cords form a spongy network spread on a mesh of reticular fibers, which are not evident with the stain used.

PLATE 41 (Fig. 2).   **SPLEEN: RED AND WHITE PULP**

This illustration shows the relation of white to red pulp. Entities in the white pulp are: the germinal center (9) of a splenic corpuscle, composed of lymphocytes and lymphoblasts; the cortical area of a splenic corpuscle (8), composed of more densely packed lymphocytes; and an asymmetrically placed central artery (10).

Entities in the red pulp are: the splenic cords of Billroth (6); the venous sinuses (2, 7), and pulp arteries (3, 11).

Trabeculae (1, 4) carrying trabecular arteries (1) and veins (4) are shown. These vessels have an intima and media, but no adventitia is apparent; connective tissue of the trabecula surrounds the media.

PLATE 41 (Fig. 3).   **DEVELOPMENT OF LYMPHOCYTES AND RELATED CELLS**

The cells shown here may be found in lymph nodes, spleen and other lymphatic tissues, originating from reticular cells or a progenitor derived from reticular cells.

The large, highly phagocytic macrophage (1), usually ranging from $25\text{-}35\mu$, shows an eccentric nucleus, vacuoles in the cytoplasm (due to dissolved lipid inclusions), fragments of ingested nuclei, and a larger unidentified inclusion.

The lymphoblast (2), about $15\text{-}20\mu$ in diameter, has basophilic cytoplasm, a rounded nucleus with delicate chromatin filaments and two or more nucleoli. In the medium sized lymphocyte (prolymphocyte, $12\text{-}15\mu$ in diameter) (3), cytoplasm is less basophilic, nuclear chromatin is condensing, nucleoli are indistinct or absent. In the small lymphocyte ($6\text{-}12\mu$ in diameter) (4), cytoplasm is reduced; it may contain azurophilic granules. Nuclear chromatin is in small clusters which stain deeply.

In a plasmablast ($16\text{-}20\mu$ in diameter) (5), nuclear chromatin forms a heavier reticulum than in a lymphoblast. In a proplasmablast ($12\text{-}18\mu$ in diameter) (6), cytoplasm is more deeply basophilic than in a prolymphocyte, the nucleus is eccentric, its chromatin clumps are heavier. The plasma cell (mature plasmacyte) (7) is oval, has abundant deeply basophilic cytoplasm except for a light halo near the small, eccentrically placed nucleus. The "cart wheel" arrangement of chromatin is distinctive.

A monoblast ($18\text{-}20\mu$) (8) is much like a lymphoblast. The monocyte ($15\text{-}18\mu$) (9) has a bean-shaped or deeply indented nucleus with chromatin in filaments and strands. The ample cytoplasm may contain fine azurophilic granules (10).

PLATE 41.   SPLEEN (Panoramic View)

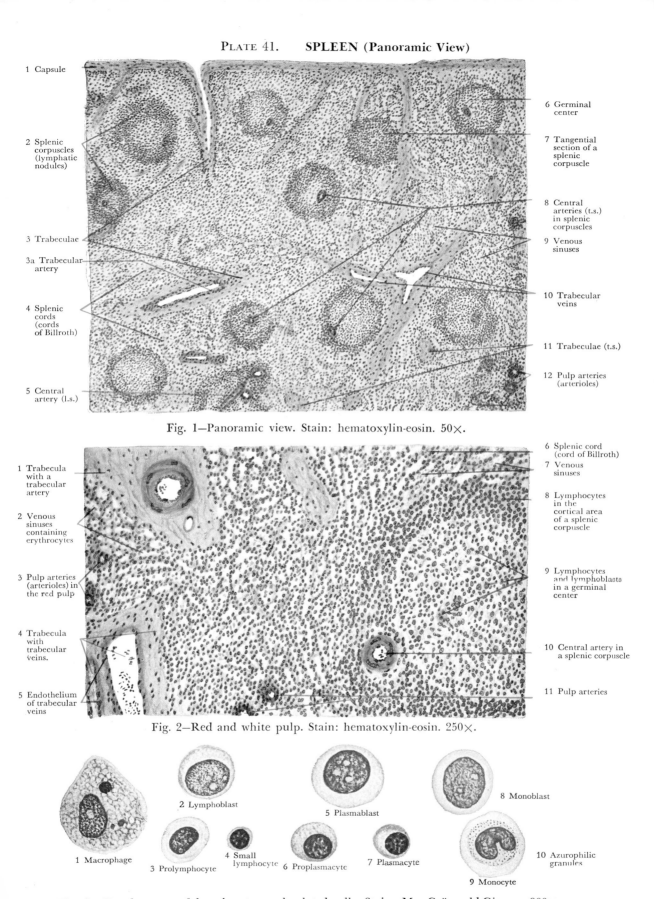

1 Capsule

2 Splenic
  corpuscles
  (lymphatic
  nodules)

3 Trabeculae

3a Trabecular
   artery

4 Splenic
  cords
  (cords
  of Billroth)

5 Central
  artery (l.s.)

6 Germinal
  center

7 Tangential
  section of a
  splenic
  corpuscle

8 Central
  arteries (t.s.)
  in splenic
  corpuscles

9 Venous
  sinuses

10 Trabecular
   veins

11 Trabeculae (t.s.)

12 Pulp arteries
   (arterioles)

Fig. 1—Panoramic view. Stain: hematoxylin-eosin. 50×.

1 Trabecula
  with a
  trabecular
  artery

2 Venous
  sinuses
  containing
  erythrocytes

3 Pulp arteries
  (arterioles) in
  the red pulp

4 Trabecula
  with
  trabecular
  veins.

5 Endothelium
  of trabecular
  veins

6 Splenic cord
  (cord of Billroth)

7 Venous
  sinuses

8 Lymphocytes
  in the
  cortical area
  of a splenic
  corpuscle

9 Lymphocytes
  and lymphoblasts
  in a germinal
  center

10 Central artery in
   a splenic corpuscle

11 Pulp arteries

Fig. 2—Red and white pulp. Stain: hematoxylin-eosin. 250×.

1 Macrophage

2 Lymphoblast

3 Prolymphocyte

4 Small
  lymphocyte

5 Plasmablast

6 Proplasmacyte

7 Plasmacyte

8 Monoblast

9 Monocyte

10 Azurophilic
   granules

Fig. 3 — Development of lymphocytes and related cells. Stain: May-Grünwald-Giemsa. 800×.

PLATE 42 (Fig. 1)

THYMUS (PANORAMIC VIEW)

The thymus has a lobular structure. From the capsule (1), trabeculae (2, 12) penetrate into the organ dividing it into lobules (5) in each of which there is a cortex (3) and a medulla (4). The lobular divisions are often incomplete (6) so that the medulla is continuous from one lobule to another (7).

The cells of the thymus are small lymphocytes (thymocytes). In the cortex they are densely aggregated (3) but do not form nodules. In the medulla (4, 7) they are less densely packed, thus giving a lighter appearance to this area. In the medulla are thymic corpuscles (Hassell's corpuscles) (9), which are spherical aggregations of flattened cells, often showing degenerative changes in the center.

The stroma resembles reticular connective tissue but is of endodermal-epithelial origin (see 6, 9, 10 in Fig. 2).

PLATE 42 (Fig. 2)

THYMUS (SECTIONAL VIEW)

Part of a lobule is illustrated. The dense lymphoid tissue of the cortex (4) contrasts with the diffuse lymphoid tissue of the medulla (5).

The lymphoid cells (thymocytes) are seen in both areas. The cells of the reticular stroma (6, 9, 10) and a Hassall's corpuscle (7) are visible in the medulla. The corpuscle (7) is formed by flattened cells concentrically placed around a prominent central eosinophilic globule.

Small blood vessels (1, 2) can be seen in the interlobular trabeculae (3).

PLATE 42

THYMUS

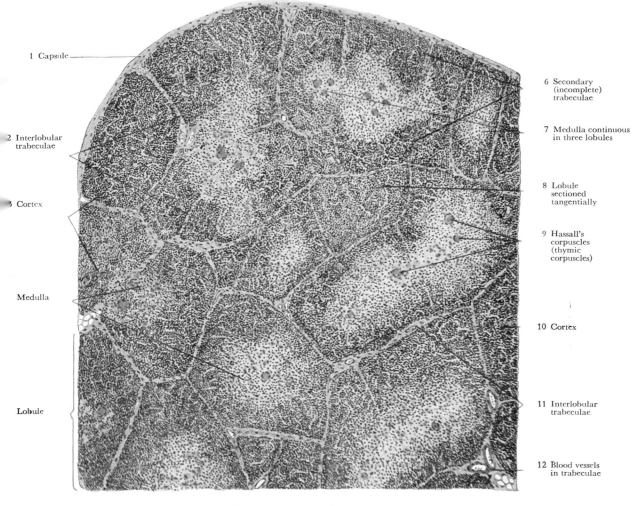

1 Capsule

2 Interlobular trabeculae

3 Cortex

Medulla

Lobule

6 Secondary (incomplete) trabeculae

7 Medulla continuous in three lobules

8 Lobule sectioned tangentially

9 Hassall's corpuscles (thymic corpuscles)

10 Cortex

11 Interlobular trabeculae

12 Blood vessels in trabeculae

FIG. 1. — *Panoramic view.*
Stain: hematoxylin-eosin. 40×.

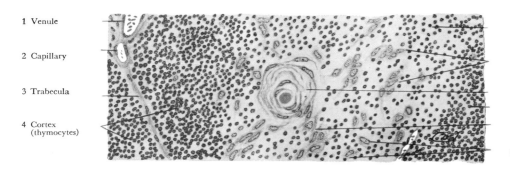

1 Venule

2 Capillary

3 Trabecula

4 Cortex (thymocytes)

5 Medulla (thymocytes)

6 Aggregations of "reticular" cells

7 Hassall's (thymic) corpuscle
8 Thymocytes in the cortex
9 "Reticular" cells

10 Isolated "reticular" cells

FIG. 2. — *Sectional view.*
Stain: hematoxylin-eosin. 250×.

PLATE 43 (Fig. 1)

PALATINE TONSIL

The surface of a palatine tonsil is a stratified squamous epithelium (1). In the underlying lamina propria lie numerous lymph nodules (2) distributed along deep and ramified crypts (3, 10). In some places, neighboring nodules merge (8), and in many a germinal center (7) is present.

The deeper regions show fibrous connective tissue (11), from which septa arise which separate one lymph nodule from another (9). Under the fibrous capsule striated muscle fibers (6, 12) belonging to the underlying muscles can be seen.

PLATE 43 (Fig. 2)

PEYER'S PATCH

In the wall of the ileum, and occasionally elsewhere in the small intestine, along the side opposite the supporting mesentery, are aggregates of lymph nodules (4). Each aggregate, consisting of many lymph nodules (10–70), is called a Peyer's Patch.

In the accompanying illustration, a portion of a Peyer's Patch is seen at (4). The cortical areas of two nodules have merged. Germinal centers (5), where medium and large lymphocytes predominate, are present.

These lymphatic formations may lie wholly with the lamina propria (2, 9) as seen here, but more commonly, they penetrate the muscularis mucosae and encroach into the tissue of the submucosa, where they may spread out to a greater size than at their origin in the lamina propria.

Villi are absent over the nodules of a Peyer's Patch when they become so large that they reach the surface of the mucosa.

PLATE 43

PALATINE TONSIL

Epithelium

2 Lymph nodules

3 Crypts

4 Epithelial tissue of crypt (tg. s.)
5 Internodular septum (trabecula)

6 Striated muscle fibers

7 Germinal center

8 Merging nodules

9 Internodular septum (trabecula)

10 Fundi of crypts

11 Connective tissue with blood vessel

12 Striated muscle fibers

FIG. 1. — *Palatine tonsil.*
Stain: hematoxylin-eosin. 32×.

PEYER'S PATCH

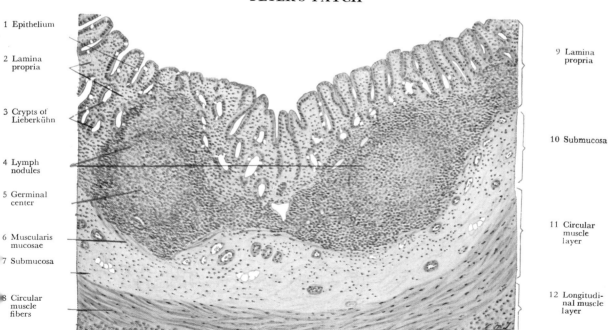

1 Epithelium

2 Lamina propria

3 Crypts of Lieberkühn

4 Lymph nodules

5 Germinal center

6 Muscularis mucosae

7 Submucosa

8 Circular muscle fibers

9 Lamina propria

10 Submucosa

11 Circular muscle layer

12 Longitudinal muscle layer

FIG. 2. — *Peyer's patch.*
Stain: hematoxylin-eosin. 60×.

PLATE 44 (Fig. 1)

INTEGUMENT: SKIN, GENERAL BODY SURFACE
(CAJAL'S TRICHROME STAIN)

The skin is composed of two principal layers: epidermis and dermis. In this illustration is seen a section of skin such as occurs on the general body surface where there is not much wear and tear. The epidermis (1), of stratified squamous epithelium, is thin, and shows only a stratum corneum (5) and a stratum germinativum (6). The narrow zone of fine-fibered dense irregular connective tissue is the papillary layer (2) of the dermis. Its projections into the basal epidermis are the dermal papillae (7). The reticular layer (3), of heavy, dense, irregular connective tissue, comprises the bulk of the dermis. A small portion of hypodermis, the superficial region of the underlying subcutaneous tissue (4), is seen.

The accessory structures of the skin lie, for the most part, in the dermis. Shown here are scattered hair follicles and a sweat gland, whose structure is seen in more detail in Plate 45. The lower part of a hair follicle in longitudinal section (12) shows its papilla and hair bulb at its base in the deepest part of the dermis. The upper part of another follicle (8) shows its arrector pili (smooth) muscle (9) and a sebaceous gland (10). At (13) is an oblique section of a hair follicle in the subcutaneous tissue.

A group of tubules in the deep dermis are cross-sections through the coiled portion of a sweat gland; those sections with lightly-stained epithelium (11a) are through the secreting portion; those with more deeply-stained epithelium (11b) are through the duct.

Cajal's trichrome stain emphasizes the variations in density of collagenous fibers, and distinguishes clearly between muscle and connective tissue. Aniline dyes are used to stain the nuclei and cytoplasm. The nuclei are stained bright red by basic fuchsin. Indigo carmine in picric acid solution is used to stain the cytoplasm, which takes on an orange hue. Collagenous fibers stain deep blue.

PLATE 44 (Fig. 2)

SKIN, PALM: SUPERFICIAL LAYERS

A section of the skin of the palm is shown. Here both epidermis and dermis are much thicker than in Fig. 1 above. The epidermis, in addition to being thicker, has a more complex structure, in that five layers or zones are recognizable. The outer stratum corneum (1) is a wide zone of layers of dead, flattened cells which are constantly desquamating off the surface (10). Beneath it, stained red, is the thin stratum lucidum (2). At a higher magnification, one can sometimes distinguish faint outlines of flattened clear cells and eleidin droplets. Under the stratum lucidum is the stratum granulosum (3); its cells have keratohyalin granules, stained darkly, which can be observed more clearly at higher magnification (7).

Below this is the thick stratum germinativum (stratum Malpighii) which is subdivided into the stratum spinosum (4), comprised of layers of polyhedral cells, and a basal layer (5) or stratum basale (cylindricum) of columnar cells which rests on the dermis. Cells of the stratum spinosum were considered formerly to be connected by intercellular bridges (8), but electron microscopy has demonstrated that these bridges are blunt, intermeshed cellular projections (9). Mitosis (12) is often seen in these two deep layers. In the epidermis are several circular areas (11) which represent sections through the spiral part of the duct of a sweat gland.

A Meissner corpuscle (13) with its nerve fiber is shown in one of the papillae.

PLATE 44

INTEGUMENT

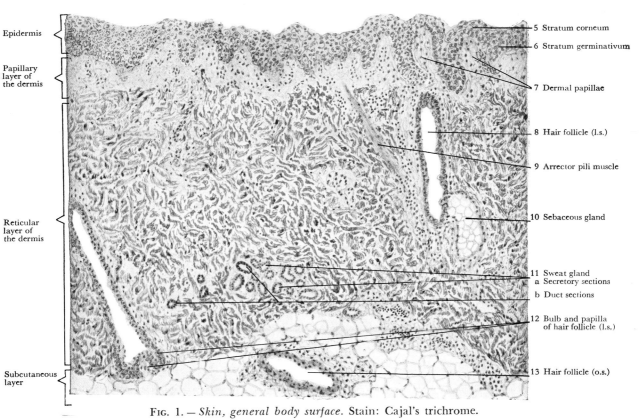

Epidermis

Papillary
layer of
the dermis

Reticular
layer of
the dermis

Subcutaneous
layer

5 Stratum corneum

6 Stratum germinativum

7 Dermal papillae

8 Hair follicle (l.s.)

9 Arrector pili muscle

10 Sebaceous gland

11 Sweat gland
a Secretory sections

b Duct sections

12 Bulb and papilla
of hair follicle (l.s.)

13 Hair follicle (o.s.)

FIG. 1. — *Skin, general body surface.* Stain: Cajal's trichrome.
Cytoplasm: orange; nuclei: bright red; collagenous fibers: deep blue. About 50×.

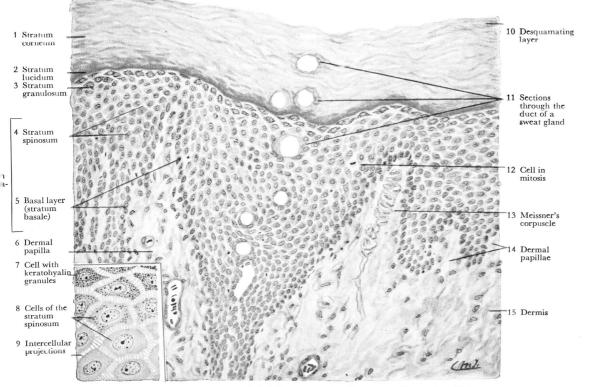

1 Stratum
corneum

2 Stratum
lucidum
3 Stratum
granulosum

4 Stratum
spinosum

5 Basal layer
(stratum
basale)

6 Dermal
papilla

7 Cell with
keratohyalin
granules

8 Cells of the
stratum
spinosum

9 Intercellular
projections

10 Desquamating
layer

11 Sections
through the
duct of a
sweat gland

12 Cell in
mitosis

13 Meissner's
corpuscle

14 Dermal
papillae

15 Dermis

FIG. 2. — *Skin, palm: superficial layers.* Stain: hematoxylin-eosin. 200×.

PLATE 45

INTEGUMENT

(Fig. 1) SKIN: SCALP

This section of skin shows a stratum corneum (1) and a stratum germinativum (2), with extensive cornification of the superficial cells.

Characteristic dermal papillae (3) are seen. The thin papillary layer of the dermis is scarcely apparent. The thick reticular layer extends from just above (4) to the region of abundant adipose tissue (22) which is in the subcutaneous layer. Beneath this is striated muscle (13).

Hair follicles are numerous, close together, and are placed at an angle with respect to the free surface of the skin. A complete hair follicle, in longitudinal section (17), traverses the center of the plate. Parts of other follicles, sectioned in various planes, are seen (5, 8, 18, 20). A hair follicle includes the following structures: cuticle, internal root sheath (20), external root sheath (18), connective tissue sheath (19), hair bulb (10), and the connective tissue papilla (11). The hair passes up through the follicle (21, 17).

Sebaceous glands are sac-like aggregations of clear cells (6, 15), provided with a duct which opens into the hair follicle. See Fig. 2 below.

Arrector pili muscles (7) are smooth muscles, originating in the papillary layer of the dermis and inserting into the connective tissue sheath of the hair follicle. Their contraction is responsible for erection of the hair.

The basal portion of sweat glands (see also Plate 46) lies in the deep dermis or subcutaneous tissue. Sections with lightly-stained columnar epithelium (12) through the secretory portion are distinct from sections through the duct (9) with its two-layered, more darkly-stained epithelium. Each duct is coiled (9) in its deep portion, becomes more or less straight in the upper dermis (16), and follows a spiral course through the epidermis (14).

Pacinian corpuscles (22), found in the subcutaneous tissue, are deep pressure receptors.

(Fig. 2) A SEBACEOUS GLAND AND ADJACENT HAIR FOLLICLE

A section through the central part of a sebaceous gland is shown. The basal cells (5) with flattened nuclei, and the polyhedral secretory cells with rounded nuclei (4) are seen; the latter illustrate various phases of holocrine secretion (3). The short duct (2) opens into the hair follicle. Connective tissue surrounds the gland from which it is separated by a basement membrane.

The various layers of a hair follicle (see Fig. 3) may be identified as follows: the fibrous connective tissue sheath (7); the external root sheath (8), composed of several layers of cells, which are continuous with the deepest cell layers of the epidermis; the internal root sheath (9), composed of Henle's and Huxley's layers. These layers of the follicle are in direct contact with several layers of the hair proper (unlabelled) which cover the cortex of the hair (10) shown in yellow.

(Fig. 3). THE BULB OF A HAIR FOLLICLE AND ADJACENT SWEAT GLANDS

The bulb of a hair follicle is shown. The various layers may be identified as follows: the fibrous connective tissue sheath (7) surrounds the bulb; the external root sheath (1) at this level is a single layer of cells, which are columnar at the top but flattened toward the base of the bulb where they cannot be distinguished from the cells of the matrix of the follicle (12); the internal root sheath, composed of its layers of Henle (2) and Huxley (3); and the cuticle (4), cortex (5), and medulla (6) of the hair proper. All of these layers merge in the bulb into undifferentiated cells of the matrix (12), which cap the papilla (11) of connective tissue. Mitosis (10) is frequently seen in the cells of the matrix.

The secretory cells (9) and duct cells (8) of sweat glands lie in the surrounding connective tissue. Characteristically, the former are larger and less deeply stained than the latter.

PLATE 45

INTEGUMENT

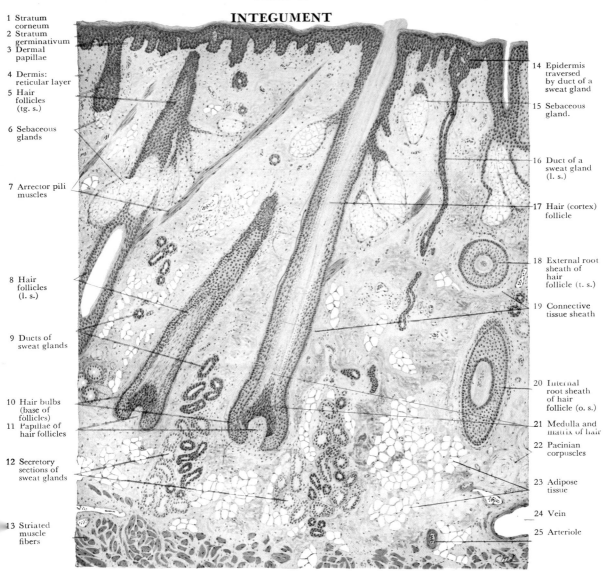

1 Stratum corneum
2 Stratum germinativum
3 Dermal papillae
4 Dermis: reticular layer
5 Hair follicles (tg. s.)
6 Sebaceous glands
7 Arrector pili muscles
8 Hair follicles (l. s.)
9 Ducts of sweat glands
10 Hair bulbs (base of follicles)
11 Papillae of hair follicles
12 Secretory sections of sweat glands
13 Striated muscle fibers

14 Epidermis traversed by duct of a sweat gland
15 Sebaceous gland.
16 Duct of a sweat gland (l. s.)
17 Hair (cortex) follicle
18 External root sheath of hair follicle (t. s.)
19 Connective tissue sheath
20 Internal root sheath of hair follicle (o. s.)
21 Medulla and matrix of hair
22 Pacinian corpuscles
23 Adipose tissue
24 Vein
25 Arteriole

FIG. 1. — *Skin: scalp.* Stain: hematoxylin-eosin. 50×.

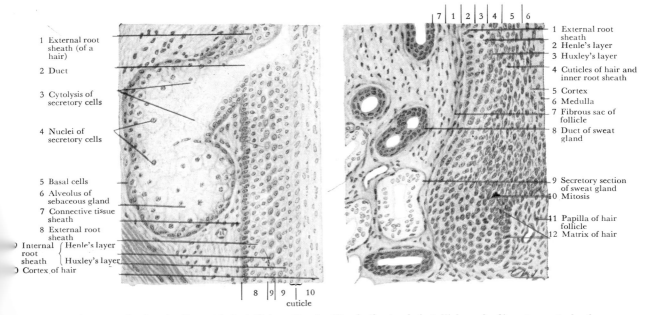

1 External root sheath (of a hair)
2 Duct
3 Cytolysis of secretory cells
4 Nuclei of secretory cells
5 Basal cells
6 Alveolus of sebaceous gland
7 Connective tissue sheath
8 External root sheath
9 Internal root sheath { Henle's layer / Huxley's layer }
10 Cortex of hair

8 9 9 10
cuticle

7 1 2 3 4 5 6

1 External root sheath
2 Henle's layer
3 Huxley's layer
4 Cuticles of hair and inner root sheath
5 Cortex
6 Medulla
7 Fibrous sac of follicle
8 Duct of sweat gland
9 Secretory section of sweat gland
10 Mitosis
11 Papilla of hair follicle
12 Matrix of hair

FIG. 2.—*A sebaceous gland and adjacent hair follicle.*   FIG. 3.—*The bulb of a hair follicle and adjacent sweat gland.*

Stain: hematoxylin-eosin. 200×.

PLATE 46

SWEAT GLAND (DIAGRAM)

In the mid-line of the plate is a reconstruction of a sweat gland. The duct follows a spiral course as it passes through the epidermis. The secretory section of the gland, indicated in light pink, is embedded in the dermis.

Sections A, B and C indicate the aspects that would appear in sections through the gland, as shown respectively.

PLATE 46

SWEAT GLAND (DIAGRAM)

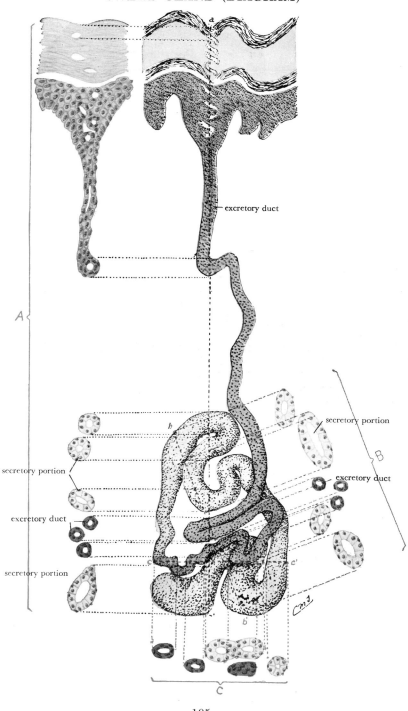

excretory duct

secretory portion

secretory portion

excretory duct

secretory portion

secretory portion

excretory duct

PLATE 47

LIP (LONGITUDINAL SECTION)

The central area of the lip is occupied by the striated fibers of the orbicularis oris muscle (8). Special stains would also reveal the presence of intertwining dense fibroelastic connective tissue. To the right of the muscle tissue is the skin of the lower lip. To the left is the mucosal lining of the mouth.

Of the skin, the outer layer is epidermis (9), composed of keratinized, stratified squamous epithelium. Beneath the epidermis lies the dermis (10). In the dermis lie sebaceous glands (11), hair follicles (12), and sweat glands (13), all of which are derivatives of the epidermis. Also to be seen are pilomotor muscles (14) and the neurovascular bundle of the edge of the lip (7).

Of the mucosa, the outer layer is nonkeratinized, stratified squamous epithelium (1). The surface cells of this epithelium, without becoming cornified, slough off in the fluids of the mouth (see Plate 2, Fig. 1). Beneath the mucosal epithelium is the lamina propria (2), the counterpart of the dermis to the epidermis. Labial glands (4) embedded in the lamina propria keep the oral mucosa moist.

Transition of the epidermis of the skin to the epithelium of the oral mucosa illustrates one of the main muco-cutaneous junctions of the body. The "red line," or border of the lip, is at (6). The surface of the epithelium of the lip and oral mucosa is relatively more smooth than that of the epidermis. The underlying papillae of the lip and oral mucosa are high, numerous, and abundantly supplied with capillaries. The color of the blood shows through the overlying cells, resulting in the characteristic color revealed. It should be noted that the epithelium of the labial mucosa (1) is thicker than the epidermis of the skin (9).

PLATE 47

LIP (LONGITUDINAL SECTION)

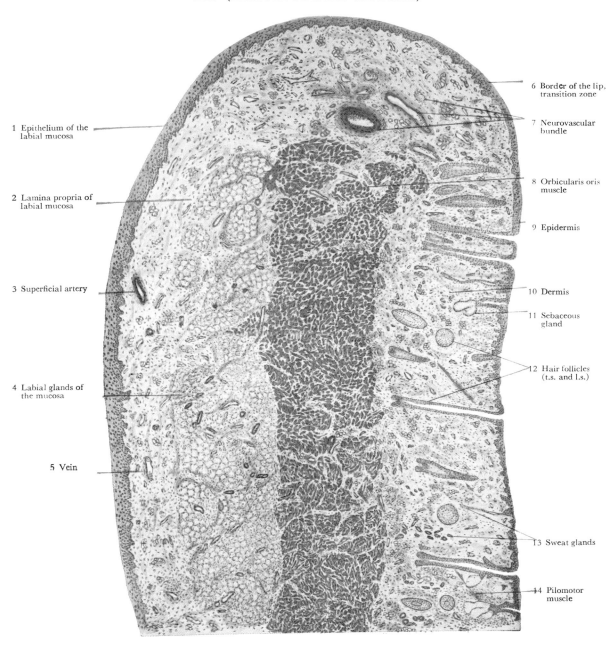

1 Epithelium of the
   labial mucosa

2 Lamina propria of
   labial mucosa

3 Superficial artery

4 Labial glands of
   the mucosa

5 Vein

6 Border of the lip,
   transition zone

7 Neurovascular
   bundle

8 Orbicularis oris
   muscle

9 Epidermis

10 Dermis

11 Sebaceous
    gland

12 Hair follicles
    (t.s. and l.s.)

13 Sweat glands

14 Pilomotor
    muscle

Stain: Hematoxylin-eosin. 20×.

PLATE 48

TONGUE: APEX (LONGITUDINAL SECTION, PANORAMIC VIEW)

The mucosa of the tongue consists of stratified squamous epithelium and a thin papillated lamina propria (1, 18) in which may be seen diffuse lymphoid tissue. The dorsal upper surface of the tongue is characterized by mucosal projections forming papillae: numerous, slender, filiform papillae with cornified tips (6) and fewer fungiform papillae (4, 7), each of which has a broad, rounded surface of non-cornified epithelium and a prominent core of lamina propria (4). Papillae are still present on the dorsal apex of the tongue [fungiform papillae (17) in this section] but are absent on the entire ventral (lower) surface (18).

Compact masses of skeletal muscle occupy the interior of the tongue. The muscle is seen typically as groups of fibers sectioned in various planes, longitudinally (2), in transverse section (3) and obliquely (5). In the interfascicular connective tissue, which is continuous with the lamina propria, may be seen numerous blood vessels (9, 10, 15, 16) and nerves (8, 17).

In the lower half of the tongue, near the apex, embedded in the muscle, is seen part of the anterior lingual gland, a mixed gland of serous alveoli (11), mucous alveoli (13) and mucous alveoli with demilunes (not illustrated). Interlobular ducts (12) pass into excretory ducts (14) which open on the ventral surface of the tongue.

PLATE 48

TONGUE: APEX (LONGITUDINAL SECTION, PANORAMIC VIEW)

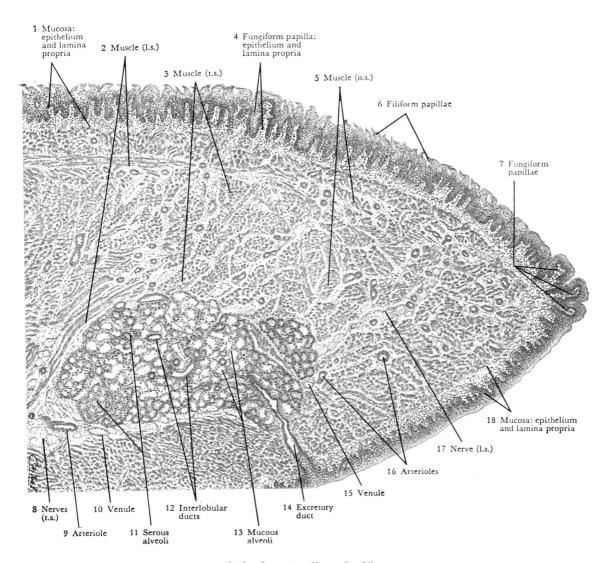

1 Mucosa: epithelium and lamina propria

2 Muscle (l.s.)

3 Muscle (t.s.)

4 Fungiform papilla: epithelium and lamina propria

5 Muscle (o.s.)

6 Filiform papillae

7 Fungiform papillae

8 Nerves (t.s.)

9 Arteriole

10 Venule

11 Serous alveoli

12 Interlobular ducts

13 Mucous alveoli

14 Excretory duct

15 Venule

16 Arterioles

17 Nerve (l.s.)

18 Mucosa: epithelium and lamina propria

Stain: hematoxylin-eosin. 25×.

Plate 49 (Fig. 1)

TONGUE: CIRCUMVALLATE PAPILLA
(VERTICAL SECTION)

A vertical section through a circumvallate papilla of the tongue is illustrated. The lamina propria, or core of connective tissue, of the papilla has numerous secondary papillae, which project into the covering stratified epithelium (7). Numerous blood vessels (3) are present in the stroma. The upper part of each circumvallate papilla does not rise above the surface of the neighboring lingual epithelium (1). A narrow groove, the circular furrow (8), separates the lateral part of the papilla from the adjacent wall (9). Barrel-shaped taste buds (4, 10) are located in the sides of the furrow. Many serous alveoli composing von Ebner's glands (11), are seen among the bundles of muscle fibers (5, 13). Sections of their ducts, which open into the circular furrow (6, 12), are also shown.

Plate 49 (Fig. 2)

POSTERIOR TONGUE (LONGITUDINAL SECTION)

This section illustrates posterior tongue about 2 cm. behind the circumvallate papillae, approaching the area occupied by lingual tonsils. The dorsal surface of the posterior tongue typically shows large mucosal ridges (1), and rounded elevations (6) or folds which may somewhat resemble large fungiform papillae. Lymphatic nodules of the lingual tonsils will be seen in such elevations. Typical filiform and fungiform papillae are absent.

The lamina propria of the mucosa is wider but similar to that in the anterior two-thirds of the tongue, with diffuse lymphoid tissue in the subepithelial zone (2), groups of adipose cells (3), many blood vessels and nerves. A large nerve is seen coursing along the vertical axis of the mucosal fold (9).

Numerous alveoli of the posterior lingual mucous glands (4) lie in the deep lamina propria and in connective tissue trabeculae between groups of striated muscle fibers (5, 10), extending deep down into the muscular mass. The excretory ducts (7) open onto the dorsal surface of the tongue, usually between bases of the mucosal ridges and folds, but in this figure, at the apex of a ridge. Anteriorly these glands come in contact with the serous glands of von Ebner; posteriorly they extend through the root of the tongue.

PLATE 49

TONGUE

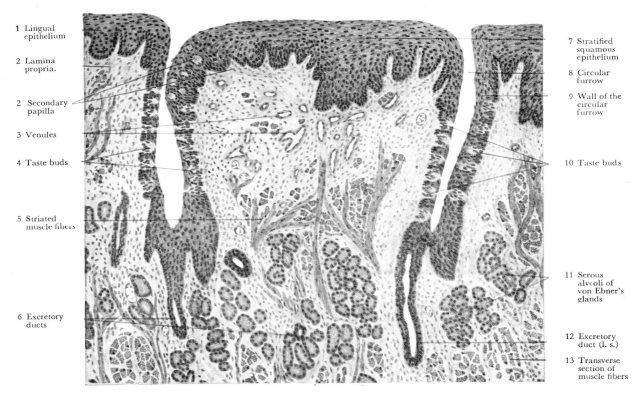

1 Lingual
  epithelium

2 Lamina
  propria.

2 Secondary
  papilla

3 Venules

4 Taste buds

5 Striated
  muscle fibers

6 Excretory
  ducts

7 Stratified
  squamous
  epithelium

8 Circular
  furrow

9 Wall of the
  circular
  furrow

10 Taste buds

11 Serous
   alveoli of
   von Ebner's
   glands

12 Excretory
   duct (l. s.)

13 Transverse
   section of
   muscle fibers

FIG. 1. — *Circumvallate papilla (vertical section)*.
Stain: hematoxylin-eosin. 115×.

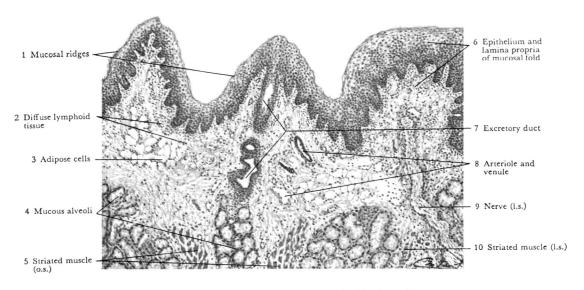

1 Mucosal ridges

2 Diffuse lymphoid
  tissue

3 Adipose cells

4 Mucous alveoli

5 Striated muscle
  (o.s.)

6 Epithelium and
  lamina propria
  of mucosal fold

7 Excretory duct

8 Arteriole and
  venule

9 Nerve (l.s.)

10 Striated muscle (l.s.)

FIG. 2. — *Posterior tongue (longitudinal section)*.
Stain: hematoxylin-eosin. 85×.

PLATE 50 (Fig. 1)

DRIED TOOTH (PANORAMIC VIEW, LONGITUDINAL SECTION)

Dentin (3, 5) surrounds the pulp cavity (4) and its extension, the root canal (6). In the living tooth, the pulp cavity and root canal are filled with fine connective tissue which contains fibroblasts, histiocytes, odontoblasts, blood vessels and nerves. Dentin (3) has wavy, parallel, dentinal tubules. The oldest or primary dentin lies at the periphery of the tooth (3); the later or secondary dentin lies along the pulp cavity (5), where it is formed throughout life by odontoblasts. In the crown of a dried tooth, at the periphery of the dentin close to its junction with the enamel, there are many irregular spaces filled with air which appear black. These are the interglobular spaces (12) which, in the living tooth, are filled with incompletely calcified dentin (interglobular dentin). Similar areas, but smaller and closer together, are present in the root, close to the dentinal-cementum junction, where they form the granular layer of Tomes (13).

Dentin of the crown is covered by a thick layer of enamel (1) composed of enamel rods or prisms held together by a small amount of interprismatic cementing substance. With adequate lighting it is possible to see the lines of Retzius (8), which represent variations in the rate of enamel deposition, and the bands of Schreger (9). Light rays passing through dried sections of tooth are refracted by twists which occur in the enamel rods as they course toward the surface of the tooth. These refracted rays appear to the eye as the bands of Schreger. At the dentinal-enamel junction may be seen enamel spindles (10) and enamel tufts (11) (see Fig. 2).

Cementum covers the dentin of the root (7). In it are lacunae (14) with canaliculi.

(Fig. 2)

DRIED TOOTH (LAYERS OF THE CROWN)

Enamel and dentin are shown. In the enamel are elongated enamel rods (1). In the enamel near the dentinal junction are seen enamel spindles (2), extensions of dentinal matrix penetrating for short distances into the enamel. Enamel tufts (3), which extend from the dentinal-enamel junction (4) into the enamel, are groups of poorly calcified, twisted enamel rods. Dentin with dentinal canals is shown (6). In the dentin are the interglobular spaces (5) filled with air and appearing black.

(Fig. 3)

DRIED TOOTH (LAYERS OF THE ROOT)

Dentin (6) and cementum (9) are shown. In the dentin, near the dentinal-cementum junction, is the granular layer of Tomes (7). Internal to this are the large, irregular interglobular spaces (8) which are commonly seen in the crown of the tooth but may also be present in the root. In the cementum (9) are lacunae (10) with their canaliculi.

PLATE 50

DRIED TOOTH

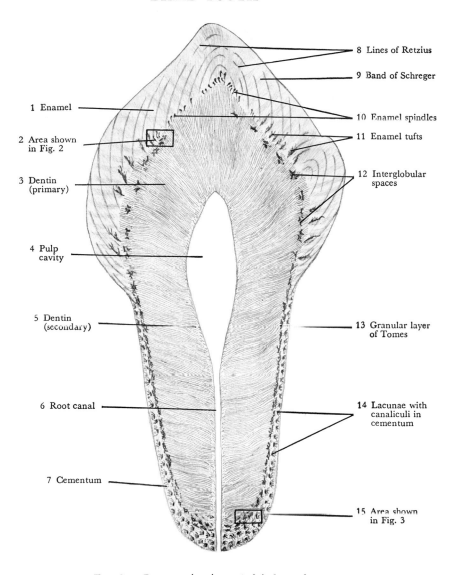

1 Enamel

2 Area shown in Fig. 2

3 Dentin (primary)

4 Pulp cavity

5 Dentin (secondary)

6 Root canal

7 Cementum

8 Lines of Retzius

9 Band of Schreger

10 Enamel spindles

11 Enamel tufts

12 Interglobular spaces

13 Granular layer of Tomes

14 Lacunae with canaliculi in cementum

15 Area shown in Fig. 3

FIG. 1. — *Panoramic view of dried tooth.*

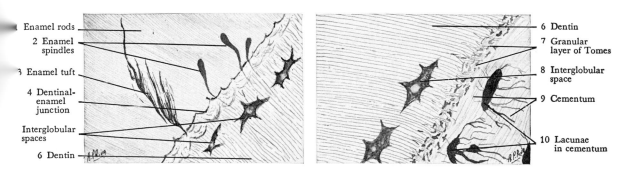

1 Enamel rods

2 Enamel spindles

3 Enamel tuft

4 Dentinal-enamel junction

Interglobular spaces

6 Dentin

6 Dentin

7 Granular layer of Tomes

8 Interglobular space

9 Cementum

10 Lacunae in cementum

FIG. 2. — *Layers of the crown. Area corresponding to (2) in Fig. 1. 160×.*

FIG. 3. — *Layers of the root. Area corresponding to (15) in Fig. 1. 160×.*

PLATE 51 (Fig. 1)

DEVELOPING TOOTH (PANORAMIC VIEW)

A developing deciduous tooth is shown embedded in an alveolus of the jaw. The dental sac (5) separates the tooth from the surrounding connective tissue (3). Enclosed within the sac is the enamel organ, composed of the external enamel epithelium (17), the enamel pulp (6), the intermediate stratum (19), and the internal enamel epithelium of ameloblasts (ganoblasts) (7). These structures form a hood-like covering over the developing tooth. The darkest layer of pink is the enamel (15), deposited by the ameloblasts.

The dental pulp of connective tissue (20) forms the core of the developing tooth. It is penetrated by blood vessels. A layer of cells, the odontoblasts (11), form at the outer margin of the pulp. The odontoblasts secrete the dentin (16), which is the broad pink layer adjacent to the enamel. Between the dentin and odontoblasts lies the predentin (10), a layer of uncalcified dentin. The predentin is more clearly evident toward the apex of the tooth (see also Fig. 2 below).

The mucosa of the mouth (1, 13) covers all the above structures. The germ of a permanent tooth (2) is seen.

PLATE 51 (Fig. 2)

DEVELOPING TOOTH (SECTIONAL VIEW)

At the left of the figure are the connective tissue cells of the dental pulp (1) adjacent to the odontoblasts (2), which secrete the uncalcified predentin (3) and the calcified dentin (4). The dentinal fibers of Tomes (3) are also shown; these are the persistent processes of the odontoblasts which were responsible for depositing the dentin and predentin.

The enamel (5), as in Fig. 1, is the darkest band of pink. In contact with the enamel are the ameloblasts (6). In the process of enamel formation the apical end of each ameloblast becomes transformed into a terminal portion, or process of Tomes. These processes then appear collectively in advanced enamel as a separate layer (9). The prismatic structure of the enamel is indicated by the fine lines, which give a striated appearance to the enamel.

Adjacent to the ameloblasts is the intermediate stratum (8), which is in turn surrounded by the stellate cells of the enamel pulp (7).

PLATE 51

DEVELOPING TOOTH

1 Epithelium

2 Germ of
permanent
tooth

3 Connective
tissue

4 Bone

5 Dental sac

6 Enamel
pulp

7 Ameloblasts

8 Enamel

9 Dentin

10 Predentin

11 Odonto-
blasts

12 Connective
tissue

13 Lamina
propria of
the buccal
mucosa (gum)

14 Muscle

15 Enamel

16 Dentin

17 External
enamel
epithelium

18 Enamel
pulp

19 Intermediate
stratum

20 Dental
pulp

21 Bone of
dental
alveolus

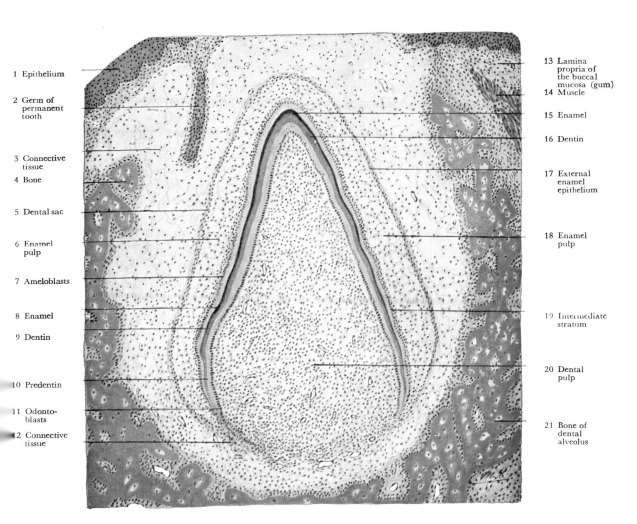

FIG. 1. — *Panoramic view.*
Stain: hematoxylin-eosin. 50×.

1 Cells of
dental pulp

2 Odontoblast

3 Predentin
and fibers
of Tomes

4 Dentin

5 Enamel

6 Ameloblasts
(adamantine
epithelium)

7 Enamel
pulp

8 Intermediate
stratum

9 Layer of
processes of
Tomes

10 Enamel
prisms
(t. s.)

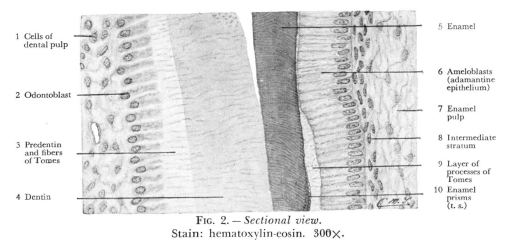

FIG. 2. — *Sectional view.*
Stain: hematoxylin-eosin. 300×.

PLATE 52

SALIVARY GLAND: PAROTID

The predominant elements in the field are the serous salivary alveoli (14 and I), formed by lavender pyramidal cells, each of which has a dark spherical nucleus at the base. The lumen of every alveolus is not in evidence. Intercalary ducts (7, 16, 20 and II) drain the alveoli and lie within the lobules of the gland. The next larger order of ducts is the striated duct (4, 6, and III). These are also intralobular ducts and stain deeply with eosin. Subsequent ducts lie in the trabeculae of connective tissue and hence are termed interlobular ducts (11, 13, IV). They have a wide lumen. The epithelium stains violet pink with component cells ranging from a low columnar type to a higher pseudostratified columnar type.

The gland is divided into lobes and lobules by connective tissue (5, 10, 12, 15), in which lie numerous blood vessels (2, 3, 8, 9). A parasympathetic ganglion (19) is easily recognized by its large cells, each with a rounded nucleus containing one or two prominent nucleoli. The thin connective tissue partitions between the alveoli or lobules show blood vessels (17) of small diameter (capillaries). Numerous adipose cells (1, 18) lie among the alveoli.

PLATE 52

SALIVARY GLAND: PAROTID

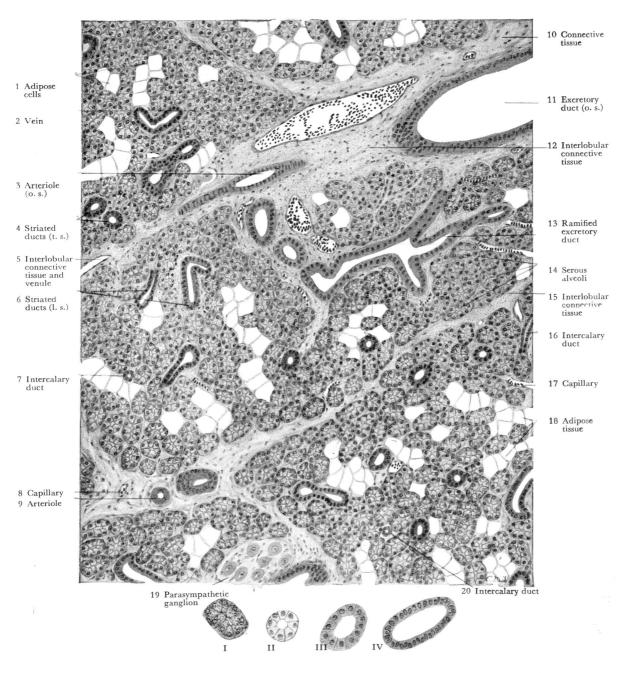

1 Adipose cells

2 Vein

3 Arteriole (o. s.)

4 Striated ducts (t. s.)

5 Interlobular connective tissue and venule

6 Striated ducts (l. s.)

7 Intercalary duct

8 Capillary
9 Arteriole

10 Connective tissue

11 Excretory duct (o. s.)

12 Interlobular connective tissue

13 Ramified excretory duct

14 Serous alveoli

15 Interlobular connective tissue

16 Intercalary duct

17 Capillary

18 Adipose tissue

19 Parasympathetic ganglion

20 Intercalary duct

I   II   III   IV

I. serous alveolus; II. intercalary duct; III. striated duct; IV. excretory duct.

Stain: hematoxylin-eosin. 120×.

PLATE 53

SALIVARY GLAND: SUBMANDIBULAR (SUBMAXILLARY)

The submandibular (submaxillary) gland is composed of both serous and mucous alveoli. The serous alveoli (2, 9, and II) can be recognized by their size, the intensity and color with which they are stained by hematoxylin-eosin, the rounded subcentral nuclei of the cells, and the narrow, almost obliterated lumen. The mucous alveoli (3, 8, and IV) differ from the serous by the larger size of the mucous cells, the pale pink color of their stain, the flat nucleus at the base of each cell, and the small but apparent lumen. Mixed alveoli made up of serous and mucous cells also occur. The most typical are those in which serous cells appear to "cap" the mucous cells, forming the serous demilunes (demilunes of Gianuzzi) (7 and V).

Among the alveoli are intercalary ducts (I) of smaller diameter than the serous alveoli. The cells of these ducts are cuboid with a rounded central nucleus.

Striated ducts also occur. The aveolus which has been cut lengthwise (IV) illustrates the relation of the alveolus to the intercalary duct (11) and to the striated duct (12). Striated ducts are usually intralobular (6), occasionally interlobular (1). Their diameter is larger than that of the intercalary ducts. The cells of a striated duct are cuboid or columnar. Each stains deeply with eosin and has a rounded central nucleus. An interlobular duct (1) has been sectioned obliquely and the several branches which form it are thus in evidence.

A duct of large diameter and ample lumen (4) is seen in the interlobular connective tissue. It is lined by relatively low columnar cells, lightly stained.

Numerous adipose cells (10) and a few blood vessels (5) occur in the connective tissue surrounding the alveoli.

PLATE 53

SALIVARY GLAND: SUBMANDIBULAR (SUBMAXILLARY)

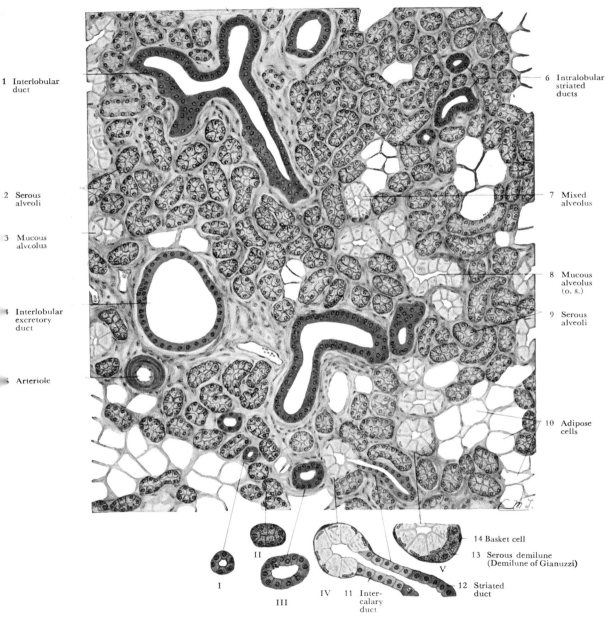

1 Interlobular duct

2 Serous alveoli

3 Mucous alveolus

4 Interlobular excretory duct

5 Arteriole

6 Intralobular striated ducts

7 Mixed alveolus

8 Mucous alveolus (o. s.)

9 Serous alveoli

10 Adipose cells

14 Basket cell

13 Serous demilune (Demilune of Gianuzzi)

12 Striated duct

11 Intercalary duct

I   II   III   IV   V

I. Intercalary duct; II. serous alveolus; III. striated duct; IV. mucous alveolus with intercalary and striated ducts (l.s.); V. mixed alveolus.

Stain: hematoxylin-eosin. 170×.

PLATE 54

SALIVARY GLAND: SUBLINGUAL

The sublingual gland, like the submandibular, is composed of mucous (4, 6) and serous (3) alveoli; in the sublingual, however, the mucous alveoli are the more abundant. Some mixed alveoli (7) also occur, in which serous cells appear to "cap" the mucous cells, forming the serous demilunes (demilunes of Gianuzzi) (2, 17).

Intercalary ducts are absent or rarely found (8 and IV). Striated ducts (1, 9, and V) can be distinguished by the presence of a lumen and a heavy eosin stain. The excretory ducts (10, 15, and VI) each have a prominent lumen with epithelium that is pseudostratified in the larger units.

Interlobular connective tissue (13) in the sublingual glands is characteristically more abundant than in the parotid or submandibular; this is largely because the body of the sublingual is not as compact as the other two salivary glands.

Between the epithelium of an alveolus and its basement membrane, there is sometimes found a type of cell (19, 21) which seems to "hold" the secretory cells. These myoepithelial cells are highly variable constituents of such glands as the salivary glands. Because these cells seem to hold the secretory cells they have been called basket cells (16, 19, 21).

PLATE 54

SALIVARY GLAND: SUBLINGUAL

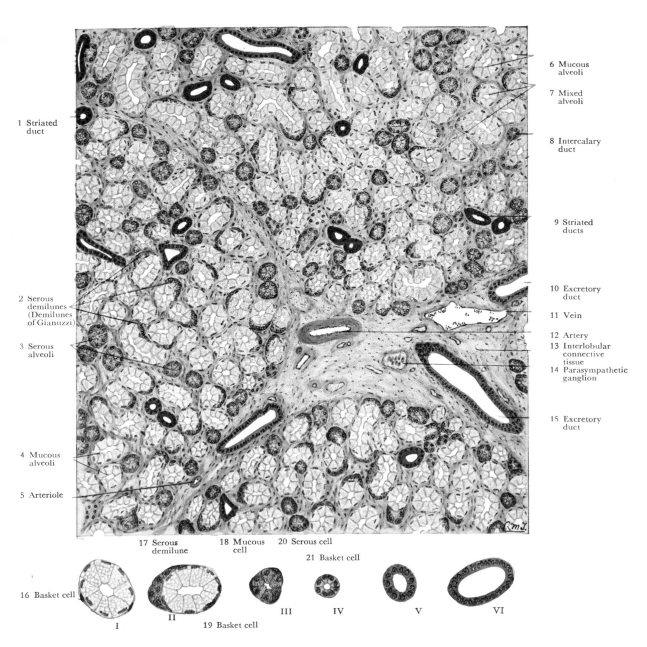

1 Striated duct

2 Serous demilunes (Demilunes of Gianuzzi)

3 Serous alveoli

4 Mucous alveoli

5 Arteriole

6 Mucous alveoli

7 Mixed alveoli

8 Intercalary duct

9 Striated ducts

10 Excretory duct

11 Vein

12 Artery

13 Interlobular connective tissue

14 Parasympathetic ganglion

15 Excretory duct

16 Basket cell

17 Serous demilune

18 Mucous cell

20 Serous cell

21 Basket cell

19 Basket cell

I   II   III   IV   V   VI

I. mucous alveolus; II. mixed alveolus; III. serous alveolus; IV. intercalary duct; V. striated duct; VI. excretory duct.

Stain: hematoxylin-eosin. 85×.

PLATE 55

UPPER ESOPHAGUS: WALL (TRANSVERSE SECTION)

The esophagus exemplifies a tubular organ provided with a muscularis mucosae (3).

The mucosa of the esophagus is composed of an inner lining of stratified squamous epithelium (1), an adjacent papillary lamina propria (2), and the muscularis mucosae (3). A few blood vessels and a small lymph nodule (9) are to be seen in the lamina propria. The muscularis mucosae is formed by longitudinal smooth muscle fibers, which here have been cut in cross-section.

In the submucosa (4) lie numerous glandular mucous alveoli (11) of the esophageal glands. Ducts of the esophageal glands (10) traverse the mucosa and open into the lumen of the esophagus (cf. Plate 56). Blood vessels (12) and adipose cells (13) also lie in the submucosa.

Adjacent to the submucosa is a heavy muscular encasement composed of two well-defined layers: an inner layer of circular fibers (5), sectioned longitudinally or obliquely; and an outer layer of longitudinal fibers (7), sectioned transversely. In the upper esophagus, the musculature is predominantly skeletal. The peripheral location of the nuclei in these fibers is better seen in those cut transversely.

Connective tissue, the tunica adventitia (8), lies at the periphery of the esophagus. In it may be seen a neurovascular bundle (16, 17, 18) and numerous adipose cells (15). The artery (16), sectioned obliquely, illustrates the usual thick wall in contrast to the thin wall of the accompanying vein (17). The endothelial lining of both vessels is clearly visible. Nerves (18), cut transversely, are easily recognized as aggregations of smaller units (nerve fibers) surrounded by a capsule, the epineurium.

PLATE 55

UPPER ESOPHAGUS: WALL (TRANSVERSE SECTION)

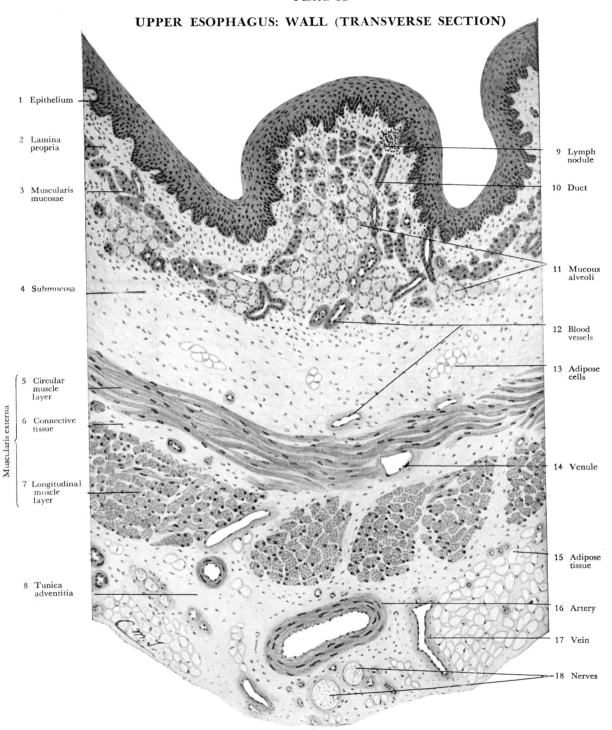

1 Epithelium

2 Lamina propria

3 Muscularis mucosae

4 Submucosa

Muscularis externa

5 Circular muscle layer

6 Connective tissue

7 Longitudinal muscle layer

8 Tunica adventitia

9 Lymph nodule

10 Duct

11 Mucous alveoli

12 Blood vessels

13 Adipose cells

14 Venule

15 Adipose tissue

16 Artery

17 Vein

18 Nerves

Stain: hematoxylin-eosin. 50✕.

Plate 56

UPPER ESOPHAGUS: MUCOSA (TRANSVERSE SECTION)

Only the mucosa and part of the underlying submucosa are shown here under higher magnification. Different layers of the epithelium can be noted: a basal layer of columnar cells with ovoid nuclei (4), several intermediate layers of cuboid cells with spheroid nuclei (2), outer layers of squamous cells with flattened nuclei (1). There are a few cells in mitosis (3) in the deep, germinal layer (4). See also Plate 4, Fig. 1.

The lamina propria (5) has many blood vessels (capillaries, arterioles, venules). An accumulation of lymphocytes is illustrated (7). The duct (9) of a submucosal gland (10) penetrates the lamina propria and opens into the lumen of the esophagus. The section passes obliquely through the duct so that at the level of the submucosa it cuts through the lumen (11), but at the level of the lamina propria it cuts only through the wall of the duct (9). The epithelium of the duct is continuous with the epithelium lining the esophagus.

The alveoli (10) of the submucosal glands of the esophagus are all of mucous nature and stain pale blue; the cells are relatively large, each with a flat nucleus at the base.

Blood vessels (12, 13), nerves (14) and adipose cells (15) are also seen in the submucosa.

In the lower left corner is the external muscular coat, composed of striated muscle fibers in the upper third of the esophagus. In the lower two-thirds of the esophagus bundles of smooth muscle cells gradually supplant the striated bundles until only the smooth type is found in the lower third.

PLATE 56

UPPER ESOPHAGUS: MUCOSA (TRANSVERSE SECTION)

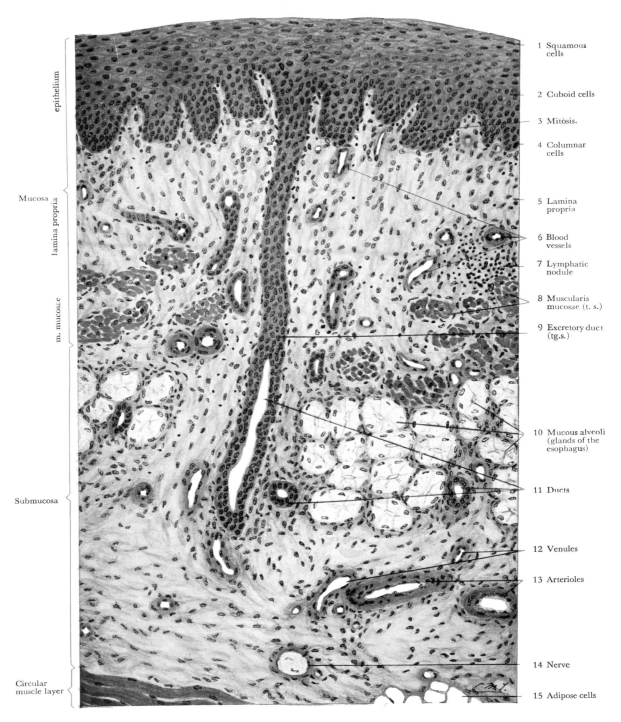

epithelium

Mucosa

lamina propria

m. mucosæ

Submucosa

Circular
muscle layer

1 Squamous
cells

2 Cuboid cells

3 Mitòsis.

4 Columnar
cells

5 Lamina
propria

6 Blood
vessels

7 Lymphatic
nodule

8 Muscularis
mucosae (t. s.)

9 Excretory duct
(tg.s.)

10 Mucous alveoli
(glands of the
esophagus)

11 Ducts

12 Venules

13 Arterioles

14 Nerve

15 Adipose cells

Stain: hematoxylin-eosin. 250×.

PLATE 58

CARDIA (LONGITUDINAL SECTION)

At the cardia, or esophageal-cardiac junction, the stratified epithelium of the esophagus (9) is suddenly replaced by the simple columnar mucous epithelium of the stomach (15). The boundary between the organs is thus clearly delineated.

In the lamina propria underlying the gastric epithelium, there are two types of glands: cardiac glands (14), with a single type of cell, which are also found in the esophagus (11), and the gastric glands (17) of the stomach. In the submucosa of the esophagus are mucous glands (10). These glands empty their secretion into the lumen of the esophagus (13) by way of ducts (12), which penetrate the muscularis mucosae.

Otherwise the submucosa shows no difference between the esophagus and the stomach; many blood vessels are seen throughout its length (1, 2, 3, 4, 5).

The muscularis mucosae of the stomach shows not only a longitudinal layer, but also an inner discontinuous layer of circular fibers which have been sectioned transversally.

PLATE 58

CARDIA (LONGITUDINAL SECTION)

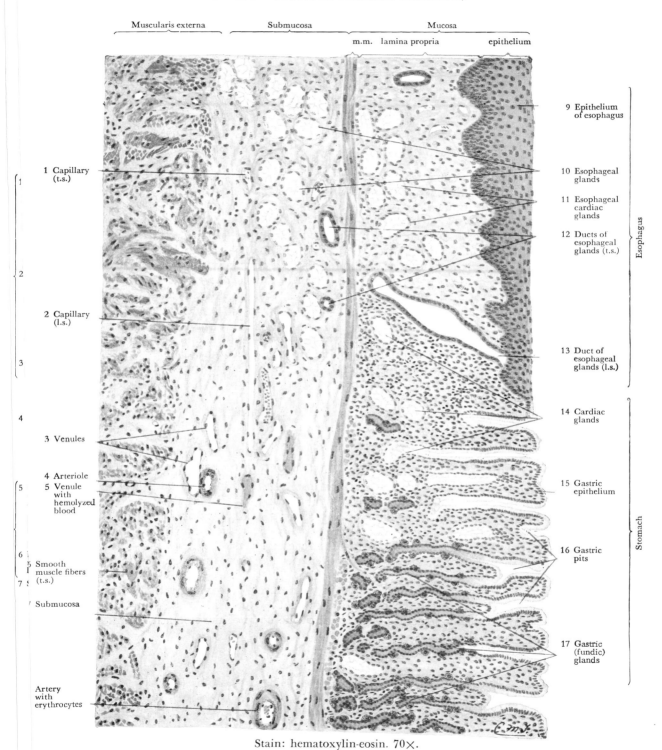

Muscularis externa   Submucosa   Mucosa

m.m.   lamina propria   epithelium

9 Epithelium of esophagus

1 Capillary (t.s.)

10 Esophageal glands

11 Esophageal cardiac glands

12 Ducts of esophageal glands (t.s.)

2 Capillary (l.s.)

13 Duct of esophageal glands (l.s.)

Esophagus

3 Venules

14 Cardiac glands

4 Arteriole
5 Venule with hemolyzed blood

15 Gastric epithelium

6 Smooth muscle fibers (t.s.)

16 Gastric pits

7 Submucosa

17 Gastric (fundic) glands

Stomach

Artery with erythrocytes

Stain: hematoxylin-eosin. 70×.

PLATE 61 (Fig. 1)

STOMACH: SUPERFICIAL REGION OF THE MUCOSA OF THE FUNDUS OR BODY

In this illustration are shown the characteristic features of the various cells which compose the superficial region of the mucosa of the fundus of the stomach. The mucous neck cells (6, 8) of the duct are cubical or low columnar cells, with pale pink granular cytoplasm, and a rounded or lenticular nucleus at the base. The cells of the epithelial lining (1) are also clear but high columnar cells with homogeneous cytoplasm and rod-like nuclei. The chief or zymogenic cells (10) are cubical or low columnar; the apical cytoplasm is granular or vacuolated, stained pinkish-blue, while the cytoplasm at the base of the cell, where the spherical nucleus is seen, is stained a darker blue. The parietal cells (7, 9) are peripheral to the mucous neck cells of the duct or the zymogenic cells of the glandular tube; they are polyhedral in shape with red granular cytoplasm; each has a central spherical nucleus.

In the lamina propria (5), the nuclei of the connective cells are visible and a few isolated lymphocytes are seen (4).

PLATE 61 (Fig. 2)

STOMACH: DEEP REGION OF THE MUCOSA OF THE FUNDUS OR BODY

The gastric glands have been sectioned longitudinally, obliquely or transversally. In the latter (10), chief or zymogenic cells (4, 12) are seen around the lumen of the gland while the parietal cells (3, 11) are not in contact with the lumen.

The inner (13) and outer (14) layers of the muscularis mucosae are also shown.

Plate 61

STOMACH: FUNDUS OR BODY

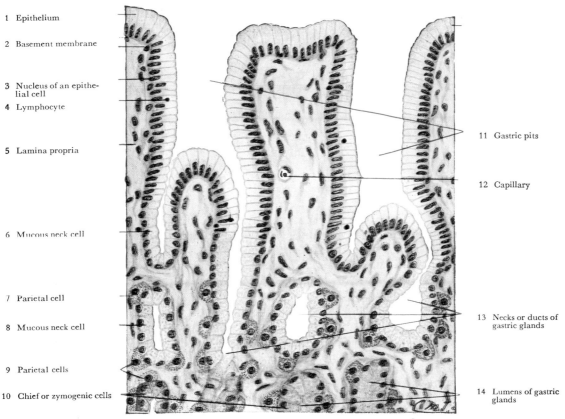

1 Epithelium

2 Basement membrane

3 Nucleus of an epithe-
lial cell

4 Lymphocyte

5 Lamina propria

6 Mucous neck cell

7 Parietal cell

8 Mucous neck cell

9 Parietal cells

10 Chief or zymogenic cells

11 Gastric pits

12 Capillary

13 Necks or ducts of
gastric glands

14 Lumens of gastric
glands

Fig. 1. — *Superficial region of the mucosa.*
Stain: hematoxylin-eosin. 350×.

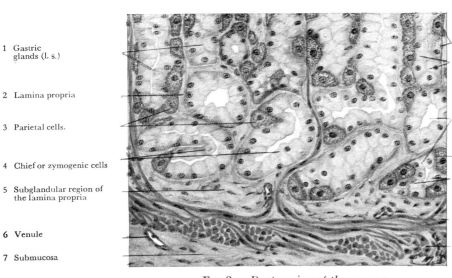

1 Gastric
glands (l. s.)

2 Lamina propria

3 Parietal cells.

4 Chief or zymogenic cells

5 Subglandular region of
the lamina propria

6 Venule

7 Submucosa

8 Parietal cells

9 Chief or zymogenic cells

10 Gastric glands (t. s.)

11 Parietal cell

12 Chief or zymogenic cells

13 Muscularis mucosae
(circular layer)

14 Muscularis mucosae
(longitudinal layer)

Fig. 2. — *Deep region of the mucosa.*
Stain: hematoxylin-eosin. 350×.

Plate 62

STOMACH: GASTRIC MUCOSA OF THE PYLORIC REGION

In the gastric mucosa of the pyloric region, the gastric pits (10) are deeper than in the fundic region. The short pyloric glands (4, 5, 11) are branched or coiled tubular mucous glands and typically have but one type of cell. Each glandular cell has slightly granular cytoplasm stained light pink and a flattened nucleus at the base. The ratio of gastric pits to glands is about 1:1.

The lining (8) of the lumen of the stomach is still simple columnar mucous epithelium.

Numerous muscle fibers, arising in the muscularis mucosae, pass into the interglandular stroma (12) and into the mucosal extensions between the deep gastric pits (2). The mucosa contains lymphatic nodules (13), which lie in the deep lamina propria. They may enlarge towards the free surface or penetrate the muscularis mucosae into the submucosa. Diffuse lymphocytes are present in the lamina propria, and a few lymphocytes are seen in the epithelium of the surface (1). Arterioles (6), venules (7, 16) and capillaries (14) lie in the subglandular lamina propria and the submucosa.

PLATE 62

STOMACH: GASTRIC MUCOSA OF THE PYLORIC REGION

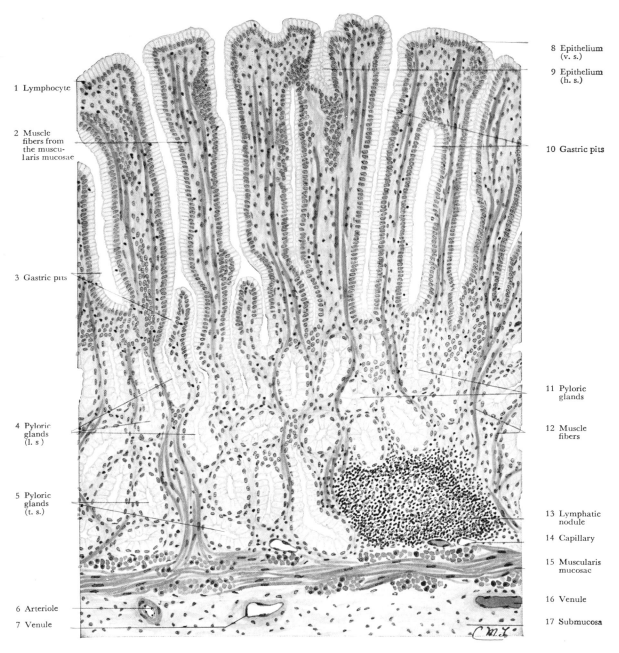

1 Lymphocyte

2 Muscle fibers from the muscularis mucosae

3 Gastric pits

4 Pyloric glands (l. s)

5 Pyloric glands (t. s.)

6 Arteriole

7 Venule

8 Epithelium (v. s.)

9 Epithelium (h. s.)

10 Gastric pits

11 Pyloric glands

12 Muscle fibers

13 Lymphatic nodule

14 Capillary

15 Muscularis mucosae

16 Venule

17 Submucosa

Stain: hematoxylin-eosin. 100×.

PLATE 63

PYLORO-DUODENAL JUNCTION (LONGITUDINAL SECTION)

At the junction of the pylorus (1) with the duodenum (2) lies the pyloric sphincter (5), composed primarily of a thickening of the layer of circular smooth muscle fibers. Frequently lymph nodules (8) are present at the juncture. Several features serve to differentiate pylorus from duodenum.

As the pylorus approaches the duodenum, the mucosal projections which surround the deep gastric pits become broader and more irregular in outline, thus assuming various shapes in sectioned material. Their free surfaces often appear grooved. Goblet cells are absent in the epithelium lining the stomach. Pyloric glands (4) lie between the well-defined muscularis mucosae (6) of the pylorus and the bases of the gastric pits.

In contrast, in the duodenum the villi are characteristically shaped somewhat like the leaf of an elm (10) and thus in longitudinal section resemble the broad surface of the leaf or any intergradation to a finger-like projection. The tips of duodenal villi are pointed rather than grooved. Between the villi are intervillous spaces (13), continuations of the intestinal lumen.

The lining epithelium makes a sudden transition from the mucous columnar cells of the stomach to goblet cells and cells with striated borders (10), which continue to be present throughout the length of the small intestine.

Short simple tubular glands, the crypts of Lieberkühn (intestinal glands), appear in the lamina propria of the duodenum (9), replacing the pyloric glands. One or more crypts of Lieberkühn open into an intervillous space (14).

Duodenal (Brunner's) glands (11) constitute most of the tissue at the bases of the crypts of Lieberkühn, both in the mucosa and submucosa. The muscularis mucosae is disrupted (12), and strands of muscle are seen dispersed among the mucous alveoli of these glands.

The submucosa is continuous from pyloric stomach to duodenum.

PLATE 63

PYLORO-DUODENAL JUNCTION (LONGITUDINAL SECTION)

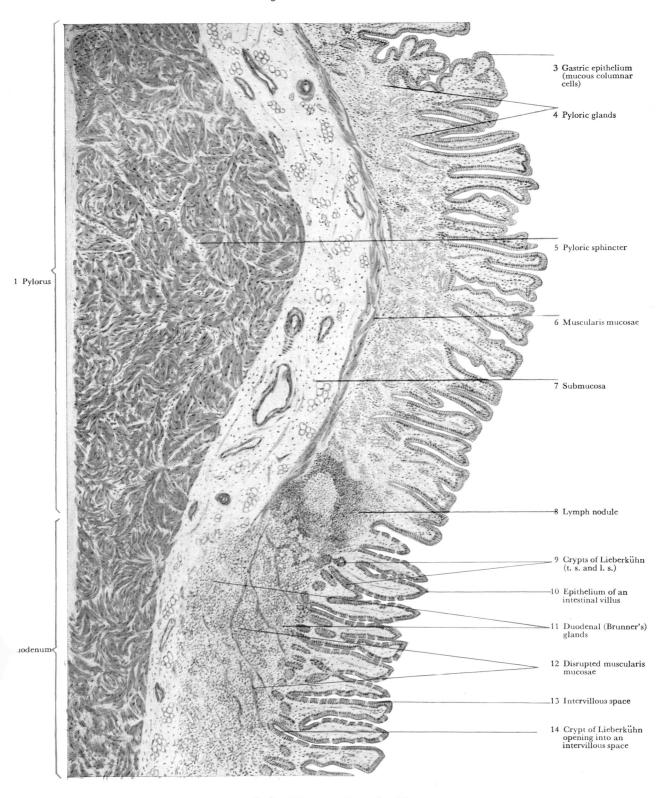

1 Pylorus

ıodenum

3 Gastric epithelium (mucous columnar cells)

4 Pyloric glands

5 Pyloric sphincter

6 Muscularis mucosae

7 Submucosa

8 Lymph nodule

9 Crypts of Lieberkühn (t. s. and l. s.)

10 Epithelium of an intestinal villus

11 Duodenal (Brunner's) glands

12 Disrupted muscularis mucosae

13 Intervillous space

14 Crypt of Lieberkühn opening into an intervillous space

Stain: Hematoxylin-eosin. 25×.

PLATE 64

SMALL INTESTINE: DUODENUM
(LONGITUDINAL SECTION)

The existence of villi (1) in a tubular organ with a muscularis mucosae (12) shows that this organ is part of the small intestine. The crypts of Lieberkühn (3, 4), also called the glands of Lieberkühn or intestinal glands, lie in the lamina propria below the bases of the villi. Characteristic of the duodenum are the duodenal (Brunner's) glands (5). The alveoli of the duodenal glands are formed by clear, mucous cells. These glands are found in abundance in the submucosa (5, 13) near the pylorus. They may be found also in the deep lamina propria (5, upper leader; 11) adjacent to the muscularis mucosae (12). Occasionally a few alveoli of the duodenal glands (Brunner's) are found in the submucosa of pyloric stomach immediately adjacent to the duodenum. The muscularis mucosae (12) is observed as somewhat branched in this region. A narrow band of submucosal connective tissue with blood vessels (7, 8) lies between the peripheral duodenal glands (Brunner's) and the muscularis externa (14). As the gut has been sectioned longitudinally, the inner circular muscle layer has been cut transversely, and the outer layer longitudinally. The majority of the fibers of the muscularis mucosae have also been sectioned longitudinally; this is due to the fact that these fibers have an oblique or spiral direction. Nerve ganglia of the myenteric (Auerbach's) plexus (9) are seen in the connective tissue between the layers of the muscularis externa.

PLATE 64

SMALL INTESTINE: DUODENUM
(LONGITUDINAL SECTION)

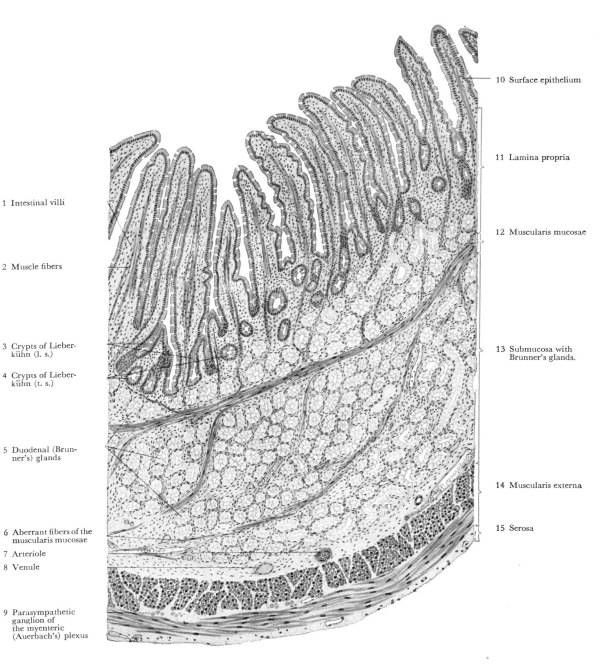

1 Intestinal villi

2 Muscle fibers

3 Crypts of Lieberkühn (l. s.)

4 Crypts of Lieberkühn (t. s.)

5 Duodenal (Brunner's) glands

6 Aberrant fibers of the muscularis mucosae

7 Arteriole

8 Venule

9 Parasympathetic ganglion of the myenteric (Auerbach's) plexus

10 Surface epithelium

11 Lamina propria

12 Muscularis mucosae

13 Submucosa with Brunner's glands.

14 Muscularis externa

15 Serosa

Stain: hematoxylin-eosin. 50×.

PLATE 65 (Fig. 1)

SMALL INTESTINE: JEJUNUM-ILEUM
(TRANSVERSE SECTION)

The intestinal villi (1), nearly all of them sectioned lengthwise, are outstanding. Some of them are retracted and have a wavy contour (14). Others, at the right of the picture, have been sectioned obliquely (13) or transversely (12).

Isolated smooth muscle fibers (15) can be seen in the lamina propria of some of the villi. The crypts (glands) of Lieberkühn (3, 16) are seen in the deep layers of the mucosa, above the muscularis mucosae (6) which they do not penetrate. The lumen of each gland is narrow, almost obliterated, in contrast to the relatively wide space of the cleft between any two villi.

A lymph nodule (20), seen here in the submucosa (7), had its origin in the lamina propria. Numerous nerve ganglia of the myenteric (Auerbach's) plexus (17) are seen between the longitudinal (9) and circular (8) layers and between bundles of fibers of the muscularis externa.

Numerous adipose cells (18) and a neurovascular bundle (19) are seen in the serosa (10).

PLATE 65 (Fig. 2)

GLANDS OF LIEBERKÜHN WITH PANETH CELLS

In the basal region of the jejunal mucosa, adjacent to the muscularis mucsoae (4), are represented the deep portions of several glands of Lieberkühn. The characteristic goblet cells (1) and absorbing cells with striated borders (2) are seen in the glands. In addition, at the base of each gland, is found a group of pyramidal-shaped Paneth cells (3). Coarse granules, which stain reddish-orange in this preparation, fill most of the cytoplasm. The nucleus and ordinary cytoplasm are displaced to the base of the cell.

Cells of Paneth are serozymogenic, but the precise nature of the products elaborated is not known. The cells illustrated here represent a storage phase, when zymogenic granules accumulate, first at the apex, then progressively throughout the cytoplasm. During digestion, cells would contain fewer granules or might be depleted; the acidophilic staining reaction would be less intense or absent altogether.

Paneth cells are found throughout the small intestine, and occasionally in the glands of Lieberkühn of the large intestine.

PLATE 65 (Fig. 3)

GLANDS OF LIEBERKÜHN WITH ARGENTAFFINE CELLS

This section was prepared from an operative specimen of ileum. Transverse or oblique sections of glands of Lieberkühn are shown. The cytoplasm and nuclei of the goblet and absorbing cells are stained with darrow red. The special silver technique demonstrates fine granules concentrated in the basal portions of some cells; the nuclei lie above these argyrophilic granules. These are the argentaffine cells (2), also called enterochromaffine cells. They are said to contain serotonin. They are found in the small intestine (duodenum mainly), in the appendix, and in the stomach.

The silver staining also reveals the argyrophilic reticular fibers (1) in the connective tissue of the lamina propria.

PLATE 65

FIG. 1. SMALL INTESTINE: JEJUNUM-ILEUM
(TRANSVERSE SECTION)

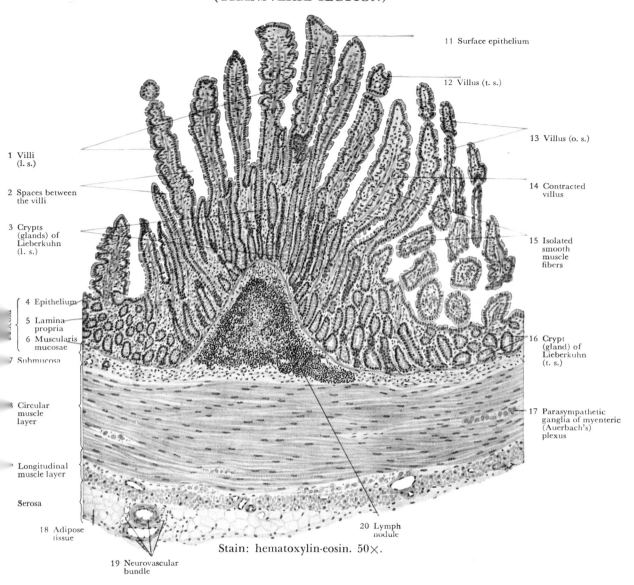

11 Surface epithelium

12 Villus (t. s.)

13 Villus (o. s.)

14 Contracted villus

1 Villi (l. s.)

2 Spaces between the villi

3 Crypts (glands) of Lieberkuhn (l. s.)

15 Isolated smooth muscle fibers

4 Epithelium

5 Lamina propria

6 Muscularis mucosae

16 Crypt (gland) of Lieberkuhn (t. s.)

7 Submucosa

8 Circular muscle layer

17 Parasympathetic ganglia of myenteric (Auerbach's) plexus

9 Longitudinal muscle layer

Serosa

18 Adipose tissue

19 Neurovascular bundle

20 Lymph nodule

Stain: hematoxylin-eosin. 50×.

FIG. 2. PANETH CELLS   FIG. 3. ARGENTAFFINE CELLS

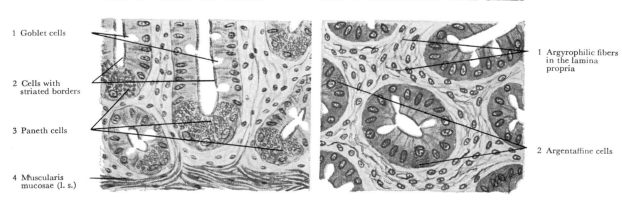

1 Goblet cells

2 Cells with striated borders

3 Paneth cells

4 Muscularis mucosae (l. s.)

1 Argyrophilic fibers in the lamina propria

2 Argentaffine cells

Stain: hematoxylin-eosin. 450×.

Stain: Fontana's methamine-silver and darrow red. 450×.

PLATE 66 (Fig. 1)

SMALL INTESTINE: VILLI

The distal parts of three villi are shown. Two are sectioned longitudinally; the center one is divided into two parts, having been folded, so that the apex has been cut transversely (1).

This magnification clearly shows: the epithelial cells (2) with the apical striated border (14) and the goblet cells (9, 10) forming the surface epithelium; nuclei of lymphocytes within the epithelium (6, 17); the basement membrane (5); the stroma of lamina propria (12) of the villus and smooth muscle fibers (16). The blood vessels are more clearly pictured in the transverse section of the villus (1). The vessel in the center of the villus (3) with an ample lumen and made up of only an endothelial layer, is the central lacteal, a lymphatic vessel. The other smaller vessels, close to the lacteal or the basal membrane, are capillaries (11). Isolated smooth muscle fibers (4) have been sectioned transversally.

PLATE 66 (Fig. 2)

LARGE INTESTINE: CRYPTS OF LIEBERKÜHN

Villi are absent in the large intestine, thus the free surface tends to be smooth (see Plate 67). It is indented by the long, straight glands (crypts) of Lieberkühn which extend down to the muscularis mucosae.

The illustration shows the region of the lamina propria immediately adjacent to the muscularis mucosae. The bases of the crypts of Lieberkühn are shown, some sectioned longitudinally (1), others obliquely (2); in the latter case the cells of the deeper part have been sectioned transversally owing to the oblique direction of the section. Some columnar epithelial cells have a slight striated border (5); many others, those with pale oval vacuoles, are goblet cells. There are a few intra-epithelial lymphocytes (6) and figures of mitosis (7), which can be recognized by the central position of the nucleus and the distribution of the chromatin. The lamina propria (3) shows reticular connective tissue cells, lymphocytes, and a few muscle fibers prolonged from the muscularis mucosae (10). A venule (8), containing blood cells, is cut lengthwise. Only a small area of the submucosa (15) is visible.

PLATE 66

INTESTINE

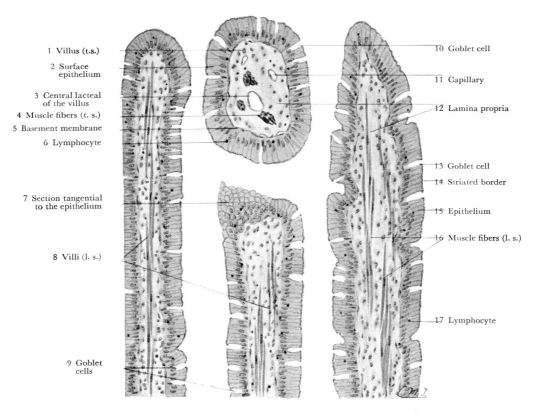

1 Villus (t.s.)

2 Surface epithelium

3 Central lacteal of the villus

4 Muscle fibers (t. s.)

5 Basement membrane

6 Lymphocyte

7 Section tangential to the epithelium

8 Villi (l. s.)

9 Goblet cells

10 Goblet cell

11 Capillary

12 Lamina propria

13 Goblet cell

14 Striated border

15 Epithelium

16 Muscle fibers (l. s.)

17 Lymphocyte

FIG. 1. — *Small intestine: villi.*
Stain: hematoxylin-eosin. 200×.

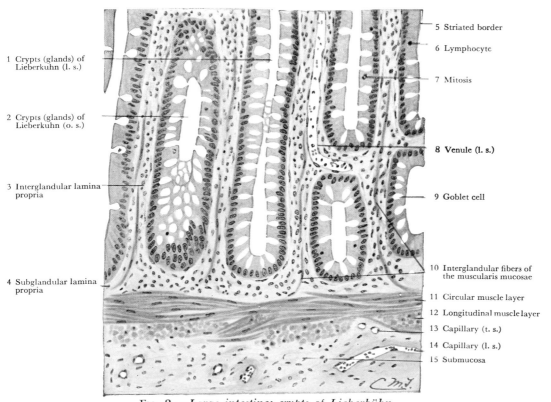

1 Crypts (glands) of Lieberkuhn (l. s.)

2 Crypts (glands) of Lieberkuhn (o. s.)

3 Interglandular lamina propria

4 Subglandular lamina propria

5 Striated border

6 Lymphocyte

7 Mitosis

8 Venule (l. s.)

9 Goblet cell

10 Interglandular fibers of the muscularis mucosae

11 Circular muscle layer

12 Longitudinal muscle layer

13 Capillary (t. s.)

14 Capillary (l. s.)

15 Submucosa

FIG. 2. — *Large intestine: crypts of Lieberkühn.*
Stain: hematoxylin-eosin. 265×.

PLATE 67

LARGE INTESTINE: WALL (TRANSVERSE SECTION)

The surface epithelium (13) is continuous with the glandular epithelium (14, 19). These epithelia do not differ significantly; the only difference between them is the larger number of goblet cells (21) in the crypts of Lieberkühn (19). The lamina propria (18) contains abundant diffuse lymphoid tissue (in a reticular connective tissue stroma). Lymph nodules (16, 23) occur in the lamina propria, displacing the adjacent crypts and occasionally the muscularis mucosae. One of these lymph nodules (16) shows a germinal center (17). Above this nodule is a crypt of Lieberkühn which has been cut through the cells of its wall (15), so that it appears as an accumulation of nuclei.

The usual layers of submucosa, circular muscle fibers (5), longitudinal muscle fibers (6), and serosa are in evidence.

PLATE 67

LARGE INTESTINE: WALL (TRANSVERSE SECTION)

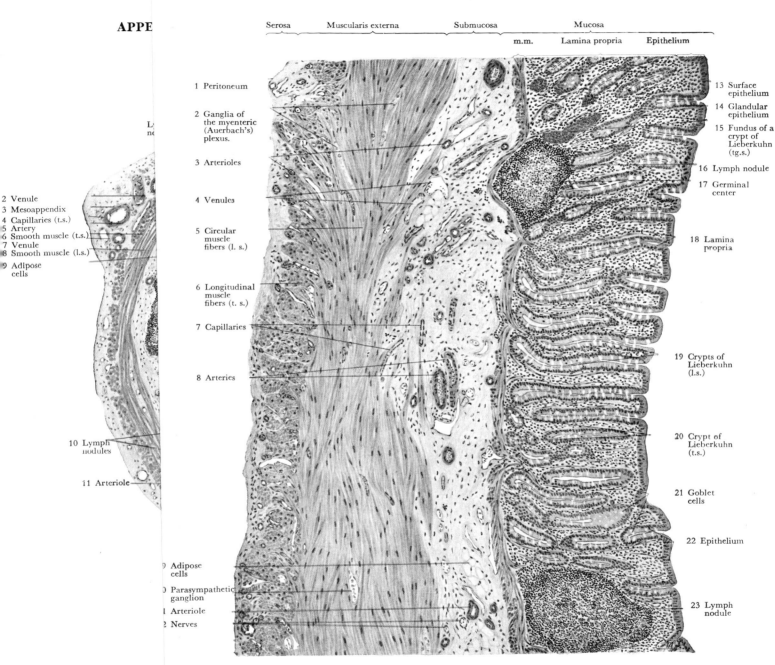

APPE

Serosa   Muscularis externa   Submucosa   Mucosa

m.m.   Lamina propria   Epithelium

2 Venule
3 Mesoappendix
4 Capillaries (t.s.)
5 Artery
6 Smooth muscle (t.s.)
7 Venule
8 Smooth muscle (l.s.)
9 Adipose cells

10 Lymph nodules

11 Arteriole

1 Peritoneum

2 Ganglia of the myenteric (Auerbach's) plexus.

3 Arterioles

4 Venules

5 Circular muscle fibers (l. s.)

6 Longitudinal muscle fibers (t. s.)

7 Capillaries

8 Arteries

9 Adipose cells

0 Parasympathetic ganglion

1 Arteriole

2 Nerves

13 Surface epithelium

14 Glandular epithelium

15 Fundus of a crypt of Lieberkuhn (tg.s.)

16 Lymph nodule

17 Germinal center

18 Lamina propria

19 Crypts of Lieberkuhn (l.s.)

20 Crypt of Lieberkuhn (t.s.)

21 Goblet cells

22 Epithelium

23 Lymph nodule

Stain: hematoxylin-eosin. 53×.

PLATE 69

RECTUM (PANORAMIC VIEW, TRANSVERSE SECTION)

hu
sta
mt
of
otl
sui
go
bu

in
pa
be
ad
bl

This section differs from those seen before because of the presence of large longitudinal folds in the mucosa, and the absence of a peritoneum and of any conspicuous lymphatic structures.

The folds are transverse sections of longitudinal ridges, called rectal columns or columns of Morgagni, which occur in the rectum. Each fold is composed of submucosa and the three layers of the mucosa: epithelium (7), lamina propria (8), and muscularis mucosae (3). Lymphocytes congregate in parts of the submucosa or lamina propria, forming small cumuli; such a cumulus can be seen above the arteriole (5).

The outer layer or adventitia (14) is continuous with the surrounding connective tissue. In the lower part of the picture there is a larger amount of this tissue with many small blood vessels (6, 16) and adipose cells (17).

The inner circular smooth muscle layer (12) is thicker than the outer longitudinal muscle layer (13). In the lower part of the rectum there is a gradual transition of the longitudinal muscle layer from smooth to striated muscle. The crypts of Lieberkühn become abruptly shorter and disappear. The epithelium lining the terminal end of the rectum also undergoes transition from a single layer of columnar epithelium to a stratified epithelium of several layers.

Parasympathetic ganglia (15) of the myenteric (Auerbach's) plexus, blood vessels (1, 5, 6, 16), and adipose cells (2, 17) are also shown.

PLATE 69

RECTUM (PANORAMIC VIEW, TRANSVERSE SECTION)

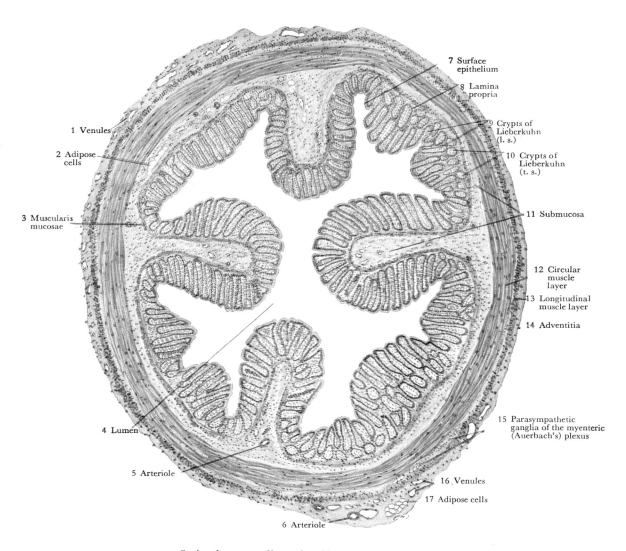

1 Venules

2 Adipose cells

3 Muscularis mucosae

4 Lumen

5 Arteriole

6 Arteriole

7 Surface epithelium

8 Lamina propria

9 Crypts of Lieberkuhn (l. s.)

10 Crypts of Lieberkuhn (t. s.)

11 Submucosa

12 Circular muscle layer

13 Longitudinal muscle layer

14 Adventitia

15 Parasympathetic ganglia of the myenteric (Auerbach's) plexus

16 Venules

17 Adipose cells

Stain: hematoxylin-eosin. 40×.

PLATE 70

ANORECTAL JUNCTION

The anatomical border between rectum and anus in a longitudinal section of the gut lies at the tip of the anal valve (8) or valve of Morgagni. This border is called the anorectal line. In gross dissections this border rings the gut as a toothed margin; it has therefore also been designated as the dentate or pectinate line. A rectal sac (unlabelled) lies behind the anal valve.

Above the anorectal line lies the mucosa of the rectum. Lining the rectum is a simple columnar epithelium (3) which is invaginated to form the crypts of Lieberkühn (6). Goblet cells are abundant. Lymph nodules (5) are frequent. A thin layer of muscularis mucosae (4) separates the connective tissue adjacent to the epithelium from the highly vascularized submucosa (7) and terminates at the junction of rectum and anus. The submucosa in turn is encased in a layer of smooth muscle fibers, the muscularis externa of the rectum (1).

Below the anorectal line lies the mucosa (anoderm) of the anal canal. Lining the anal canal is stratified squamous epithelium, uncornified (9). The submucosa of the anal canal is papillary and highly vascular. Near the anorectal line lies the internal hemorrhoidal plexus (11), with enlarged sinuses shown here at its lower limit. The network of blood vessels, however, extends well up into the submucosa of the rectum (7). Internal hemorrhoids result from the pathological extension of these blood vessels into the anorectal canal. At the lip of the anus lies the external venous plexus (not illustrated) from which may develop external hemorrhoids.

Smooth muscle fibers immediately adjacent to the upper limit of the anal submucosa constitute the internal sphincter of the anus (10). Adjacent to these fibers are the striated muscle fibers of the external sphincter of the anus, subcutaneous division (12). Two additional divisions, neither illustrated, exist of the external sphincter: the deep and superficial divisions. The levator ani muscle is designated as (2).

PLATE 70

ANORECTAL JUNCTION (LONGITUDINAL SECTION)

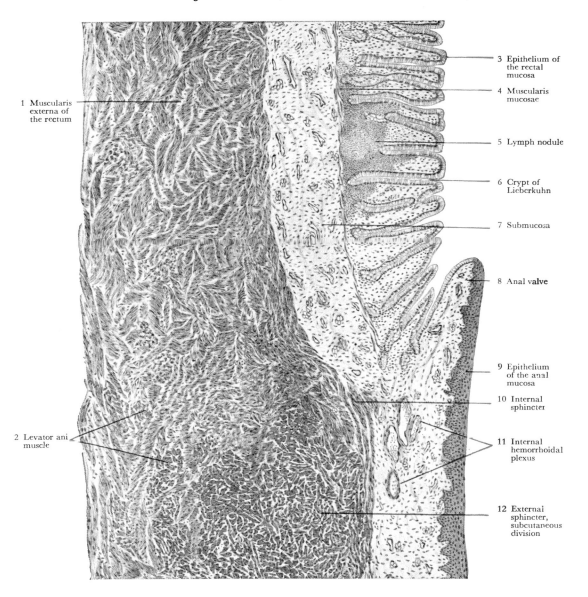

1 Muscularis
externa of
the rectum

2 Levator ani
muscle

3 Epithelium of
the rectal
mucosa

4 Muscularis
mucosae

5 Lymph nodule

6 Crypt of
Lieberkuhn

7 Submucosa

8 Anal valve

9 Epithelium
of the anal
mucosa

10 Internal
sphincter

11 Internal
hemorrhoidal
plexus

12 External
sphincter,
subcutaneous
division

Stain: hematoxylin-eosin. 25×.

PLATE 71

LIVER LOBULE (PANORAMIC VIEW)

A section of liver is illustrated, as seen under 45× magnification. One complete lobule and parts of neighboring lobules can be seen. The borders between lobules are conspicuous where three or more come in contact, at the so-called interlobular spaces, spaces of Kiernan, or portal areas (7, 14). An extension of a portal area, separating two lobules, is known as a Kiernan fissure (3). In some areas, however, no well-defined separation occurs between the lobules, the tissue and spaces of one being continuous with those of its neighbors.

In the connective tissue of each portal area or interlobular space, sections can be seen of the bile duct (6, 8, 15), branches of the hepatic artery (5, 12) and hepatic portal vein (4, 9, 13). Lymph vessels are also present but difficult to see under a low power.

In the center of each lobule lies the central or intralobular vein (10). From the center of each lobule radiate the liver plates (11, 16), with the sinusoids (17) between them. Blood from the branches of the hepatic artery and portal vein passes into the sinusoids and is deposited in the central vein.

PLATE 71

LIVER LOBULE (PANORAMIC VIEW)

1 Hepatic lobule

2 Bile duct

3 Kiernan's fissure

4 Branch of the hepatic portal vein
5 Branch of the hepatic artery
6 Bile duct

7 Portal area, interlobular space, or Kiernan's space

8 Bile duct

9 Branch of the hepatic portal vein

10 Central vein

11 Liver plate (lamina)

12 Branch of the hepatic artery

13 Branch of the hepatic portal vein
14 Portal area
15 Bile duct

16 Liver plates (laminae)

17 Sinusoids.

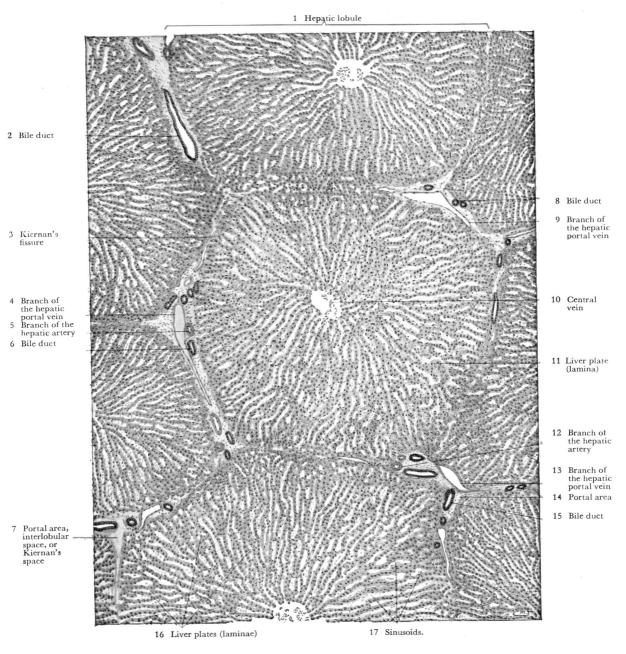

Stain: hematoxylin-eosin. 45×.

PLATE 72 (Fig. 1)

LIVER LOBULE (SECTIONAL VIEW)

Part of an hepatic lobule between the central vein (1) and the portal area is shown. The central vein contains a few erythrocytes; its endothelial lining is visible. The section passes through some of the sinusoids as they open into the central vein (2). Erythrocytes (3) and leukocytes can be seen in the sinusoids, formed by the liver plates (8). The flattened nuclei of the endothelial lining of the sinusoids can be seen on the surface of the liver cells. The liver cells are polyhedral with a single round central nucleus.

In the portal area (7) are several interlobular bile ducts (5, 11). These ducts are lined by a cubical epithelium covered with a thin connective sheath. There are also: two branches of the hepatic artery (4, 9), each with a narrow circular lumen and thick wall; a branch of the portal vein (6), with a larger lumen and thin wall; and a small, only partially visible, lymphatic vessel (10). Connective tissue surrounds the ducts and lobules.

PLATE 72 (Fig. 2)

LIVER: RETICULOENDOTHELIUM, INDIA INK PREPARATION

To demonstrate the reticuloendothelial system, a rabbit was injected intravenously with India ink; a section of the rabbit's liver is illustrated. Liver plates (3) and sinusoids (2) are shown. The reticulo-endothelial, or Kupffer cells (1, 4) of the sinusoids are outstanding owing to the engorged carbon granules, which indicate the size, shape, and processes of the cells but hide the nuclei. These Kupffer cells form a discontinuous lining in the sinusoids.

PLATE 72 (Fig. 3)

LIVER: BILE CANALICULI (OSMIC ACID PREPARATION)

A small block of liver tissue was fixed with osmic acid, sections were then prepared and stained with hematoxylin-eosin. Penetration of osmic acid into the liver tissue reveals bile canaliculi (2, 7), which exist as minute channels between cells of the hepatic plates (1, 6). The canaliculi are seen following the irregular course of the rows of hepatic cells within the plates, and branching laterally between cells. Some canaliculi are seen in transverse section (8).

As usual, between hepatic plates are the hepatic sinusoids (4, 5), seen as clear spaces, which open into a central vein (3).

PLATE 72

LIVER

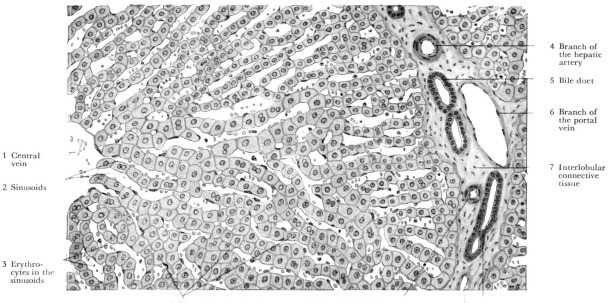

4 Branch of
   the hepatic
   artery

5 Bile duct

6 Branch of
   the portal
   vein

7 Interlobular
   connective
   tissue

1 Central
   vein

2 Sinusoids

3 Erythro-
   cytes in the
   sinusoids

8 Liver plates (laminae)   9 Branch of the hepatic artery   11 Bile duct
10 Lymphatic vessel

FIG. 1. — *Liver lobule (sectional view)*
Stain: hematoxylin-eosin. 285×.

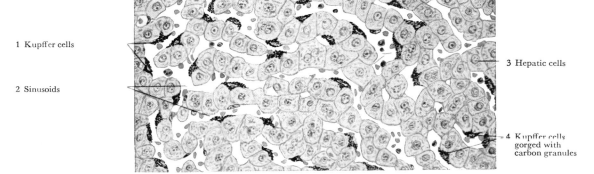

1 Kupffer cells

2 Sinusoids

3 Hepatic cells

4 Kupffer cells
   gorged with
   carbon granules

FIG. 2. — *Liver: reticuloendothelium. India ink preparation.*
Stain: hematoxylin-eosin. 350×.

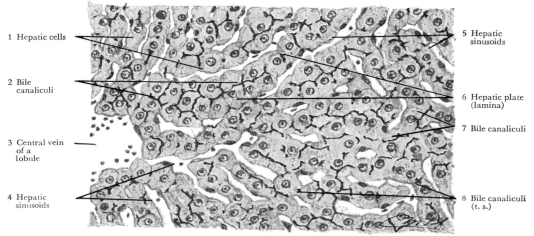

1 Hepatic cells

2 Bile
   canaliculi

3 Central vein
   of a
   lobule

4 Hepatic
   sinusoids

5 Hepatic
   sinusoids

6 Hepatic plate
   (lamina)

7 Bile canaliculi

8 Bile canaliculi
   (t. s.)

FIG. 3. — *Liver: Bile Canaliculi. (Osmic acid preparation)*
Stain: hematoxylin-eosin. 300×.

PLATE 73 (Fig. 1)

LIVER
ALTMANN'S STAIN: MITOCHONDRIA AND FAT DROPLETS IN LIVER CELLS

The specimens have been fixed in potassium bichromate and osmic acid, stained with acid fuchsin and differentiated with picric acid. The mitochondria stain red. The fat droplets usually stain black by the reduction of osmic acid by fat, but in this specimen they are blue.

(Fig. 2)

BEST'S CARMINE STAIN: GLYCOGEN IN LIVER CELLS

In sections stained with an alcohol and ammonia solution of carmine, glycogen is demonstrated in the form of red granules irregularly distributed in the cytoplasm. If the sections are stained previously with Meyer's hemalum, the nuclei take on a violet color.

(Fig. 3)

DEL RIO HORTEGA'S STAIN: RETICULAR FIBERS IN AN HEPATIC LOBULE

Del Rio Hortega uses a modification of his ammonium silver carbonate method for silver impregnation, to demonstrate even the finest fibrillar structure of the stroma of tissues. Specimens are fixed in formaldehyde, impregnated in a solution of ammonium silver carbonate, and then reduced by formaldehyde. The preparation is stained with gold chloride and fixed in sodium thiosulphate.

Reticular fibrils are stained black and the cells pale violet.

PLATE 73

LIVER

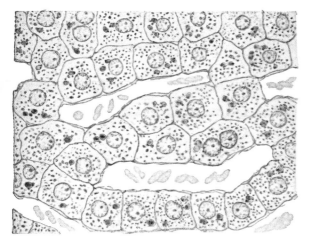

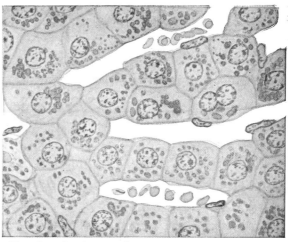

FIG. 1. — *Altmann's stain: mitochondria (red) and fat droplets (black) in liver cells.* Fixation in Champy's fluid.

FIG. 2. — *Best's carmine stain: glycogen in liver cells.*

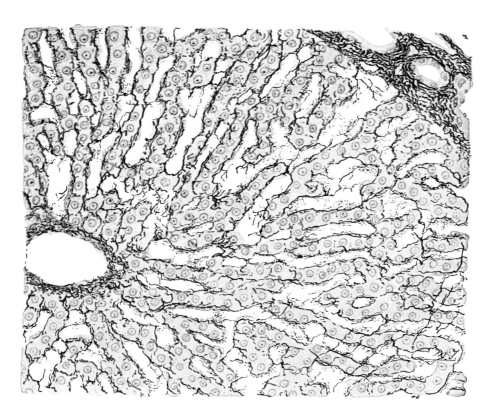

FIG. 3. — *Reticular fibers in an hepatic lobule.* Del Rio Hortega's ammonium silver carbonate method.

PLATE 74

GALL BLADDER

A section of the gall bladder is illustrated showing the folds of the mucosa which in some cases have the appearance of villi (13). These folds are present in the relaxed gall bladder but disappear in the distended gall bladder. The epithelial cells are markedly columnar, each with a nucleus at the base. In the lamina propria (4), diverticula or crypts of the mucosa have been cut transversally (15); one has been sectioned lengthwise (14), giving the erroneous impression of glands. Lymphocytes (18) infiltrate the lamina propria and epithelium.

The lamina propria (4) is composed of loose connective tissue. Peripheral to it is a layer of smooth muscle fibers (2, 7) intermingled with elastic fibers (8) and connective tissue. No muscularis mucosae exists, in contrast to sections through the gastrointestinal tract.

Peripheral to the layer of smooth muscle fibers is a wide layer of dense irregular connective tissue, the perimuscular connective tissue layer (1). Covering it is the serosa (peritoneum) (6). Where the wall of the gall bladder is attached to the liver, no serosa exists.

Plate 74

GALL BLADDER

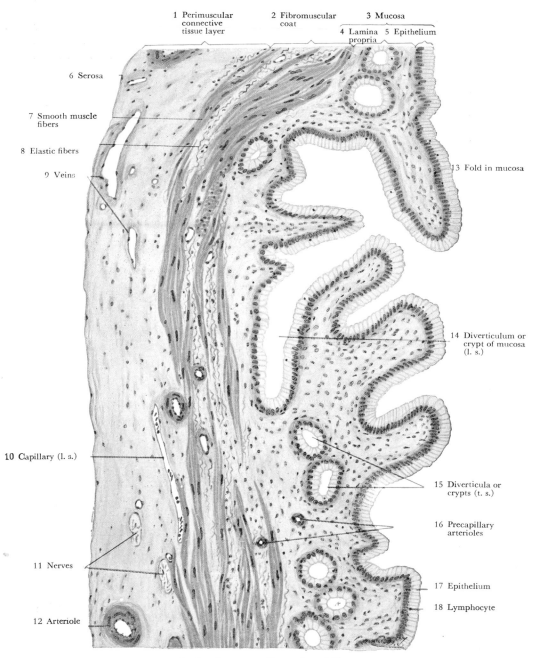

1 Perimuscular connective tissue layer

2 Fibromuscular coat

3 Mucosa

4 Lamina propria 5 Epithelium

6 Serosa

7 Smooth muscle fibers

8 Elastic fibers

9 Veins

13 Fold in mucosa

14 Diverticulum or crypt of mucosa (l. s.)

10 Capillary (l. s.)

15 Diverticula or crypts (t. s.)

16 Precapillary arterioles

11 Nerves

17 Epithelium

18 Lymphocyte

12 Arteriole

Stain: hematoxylin-eosin. 120×.

PLATE 75 (Fig.1)

PANCREAS (SECTIONAL VIEW)

The pancreas is composed of masses of serous acini (2, 15) arranged into many small, indistinct lobules and lobule groups, intralobular and interlobular connective tissue and corresponding ducts (1, 5; 10, 11), and the characteristic pancreatic islets of Langerhans (8, 9).

Observation of a pancreatic acinus (I) shows peripheral secretory (zymogenic) cells (20) and centroacinar cells (21) in the lumen. Basket cells (22) can be seen occasionally between the glandular cells and the basement membrane.

Small intralobular (intercalated) ducts in transverse sections can be seen to be made up of 6 to 8 cuboid cells (1, 5, and II). Larger interlobular ducts (11, 19, III) are lined by cuboid or columnar cells which stain more intensely.

The islets (8, 9) are rounded structures of varying sizes, but always larger than the acini. Under higher magnification (IV), they are seen to be made up of anastomosing cell columns (23) in the meshes of which are capillaries (24).

Blood vessels and nerves lie in the intralobular and interlobular connective tissue (6, 7; 10, 12, 13; 17, 18). A Pacinian corpuscle (16) is also illustrated showing its distinctive laminated structure.

PLATE 75 (Fig. 2)

PANCREATIC ACINI (SPECIAL PREPARATION)

A small field of pancreas is represented, showing cellular detail in acini after staining with Gomori's chrome hematoxylin-phloxine. Zymogen granules are stained red (1), and the basophilic substance (chromophilic substance, chromidial substance, etc.) is stained blue (2).

The upper triangle of the figure can be compared with Fig. 1 above (90×). In the lower triangle, at a higher magnification (450×), zymogen granules (1) are seen clearly, filling the apical portion of the cells (storage phase).

In the basal portion of the cells, concentration of basophilic substance and its striated appearance (2) are emphasized by the staining reaction. The nucleus lies within this zone.

PLATE 75 (Fig. 3)

ISLETS OF LANGERHANS (SPECIAL PREPARATION)

Here is illustrated an islet of Langerhans, its surrounding connective tissue (4) and a few adjacent pancreatic acini (5). Staining with Gomori's chrome hematoxylin-phloxine differentiates alpha and beta cells of the islets. Granules of A or alpha cells stain red (1), granules of B or beta cells are blue (2). Cell membranes are usually more distinguishable in alpha cells. Alpha cells tend to be situated more peripherally in the islet, beta cells, in general, lie deeper.

Capillaries (3) stand out clearly, demonstrating the rich blood supply to the islet.

PLATE 75

FIG. 1. PANCREAS (SECTIONAL VIEW)

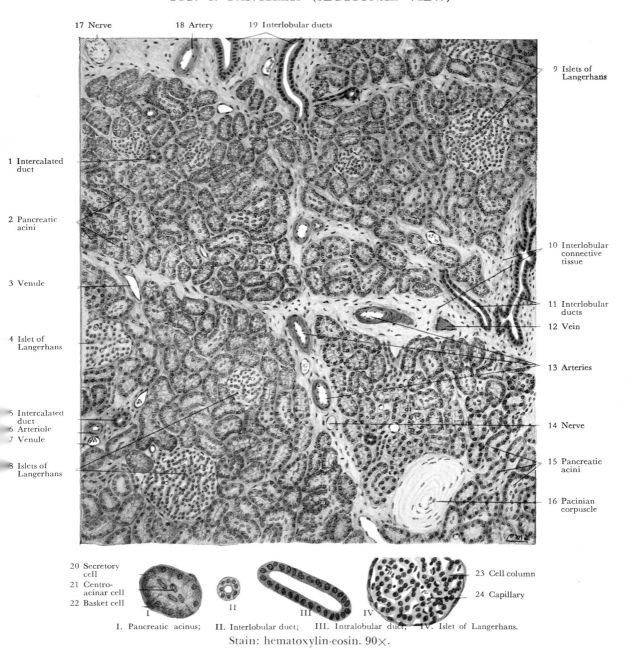

17 Nerve   18 Artery   19 Interlobular ducts

9 Islets of Langerhans

1 Intercalated duct

2 Pancreatic acini

3 Venule

4 Islet of Langerhans

5 Intercalated duct
6 Arteriole
7 Venule

8 Islets of Langerhans

10 Interlobular connective tissue

11 Interlobular ducts

12 Vein

13 Arteries

14 Nerve

15 Pancreatic acini

16 Pacinian corpuscle

20 Secretory cell
21 Centro-acinar cell
22 Basket cell

23 Cell column

24 Capillary

I. Pancreatic acinus;   II. Interlobular duct;   III. Intralobular duct;   IV. Islet of Langerhans.

Stain: hematoxylin-eosin. 90×.

FIG. 2. PANCREATIC ACINI   FIG. 3. ISLETS OF LANGERHANS

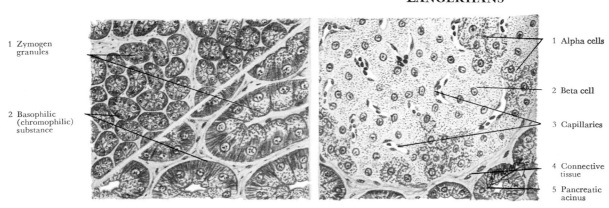

1 Zymogen granules

2 Basophilic (chromophilic) substance

1 Alpha cells

2 Beta cell

3 Capillaries

4 Connective tissue

5 Pancreatic acinus

Stain: Gomori's chrome hematoxylin-phloxine.
90× and 450×.   350×.

PLATE 76

LARYNX (FRONTAL SECTION)

The larynx has been sectioned vertically, showing its two prominent folds (13, 18–20), the supporting cartilages (8, 11) and muscles (10, 20).

The superior, or false vocal fold (13), is formed only by mucosa. It is continuous with the posterior surface of the epiglottis (12). The covering epithelium is of pseudostratified ciliated columnar type (14) with goblet cells. Mixed glands, predominantly mucous in character (15), lie in the lamina propria below the epithelium. Sections of excretory ducts (16) are seen among the alveoli; these ducts will open onto the epithelial surface. Lymphatic nodules (7) occur in the lamina propria on the ventricular side of the fold.

The ventricle (17) is a deep indentation and recess separating the false vocal fold (13) from the true vocal fold (18–20). The mucosa of its lateral wall is similar in structure to that of the false vocal fold (3, 4, 5, 6). Lymphatic nodules are more numerous, however, and are sometimes called the "laryngeal tonsils" (7). The lamina propria (3) blends with the perichondrium of the thyroid cartilage (9); there is no distinct submucosa. The lower wall of the ventricle makes a transition to the true vocal fold.

The mucosa of the true vocal fold consists of non-cornified stratified squamous epithelium (18) and a thin, dense lamina propria devoid of glands, lymphatic tissue and blood vessels. At the apex of the true vocal fold is the vocal ligament (19), a mass of dense elastic fibers. Its marginal fibers spread out into the adjacent lamina propria and into the vocalis muscle (20). The thyroarytenoid muscle (10) and the thyroid cartilage (8) comprise the remaining wall.

Passing into the lower larynx, the epithelium again becomes the pseudostratified ciliated columnar type (21); in the lamina propria are mixed glands (22). The cricoid cartilage (11) is the lowermost cartilage of the larynx.

PLATE 76

LARYNX (FRONTAL SECTION)

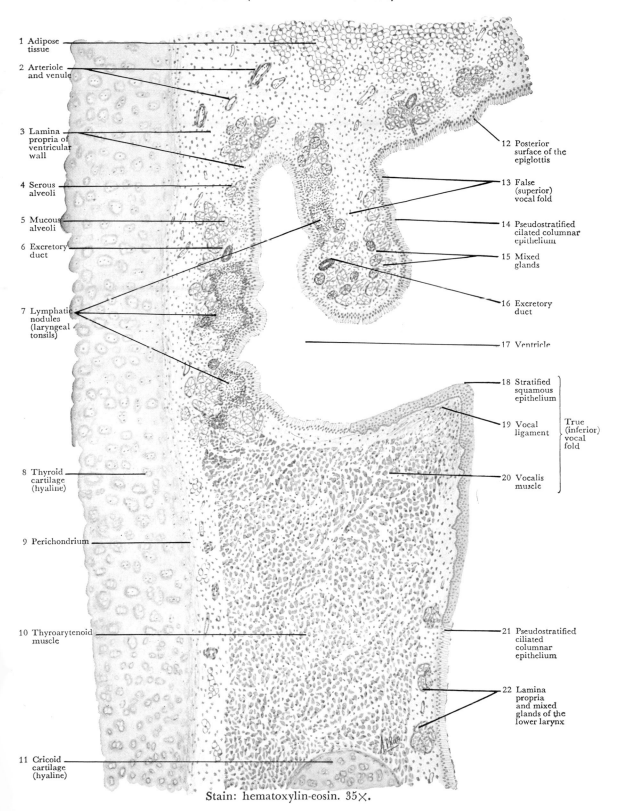

1 Adipose tissue

2 Arteriole and venule

3 Lamina propria of ventricular wall

4 Serous alveoli

5 Mucous alveoli

6 Excretory duct

7 Lymphatic nodules (laryngeal tonsils)

8 Thyroid cartilage (hyaline)

9 Perichondrium

10 Thyroarytenoid muscle

11 Cricoid cartilage (hyaline)

12 Posterior surface of the epiglottis

13 False (superior) vocal fold

14 Pseudostratified ciliated columnar epithelium

15 Mixed glands

16 Excretory duct

17 Ventricle

18 Stratified squamous epithelium

19 Vocal ligament

True (inferior) vocal fold

20 Vocalis muscle

21 Pseudostratified ciliated columnar epithelium

22 Lamina propria and mixed glands of the lower larynx

Stain: hematoxylin-eosin. 35×.

PLATE 77 (Fig. 1)

TRACHEA (PANORAMIC VIEW, TRANSVERSE SECTION)

The supporting tissue of the trachea is made up of hyaline cartilage (3), shaped like a U in a full cross section. The tracheal cartilage is surrounded by the adventitia in which lie numerous adipose cells (8), blood vessels and nerves (7). Bundles of smooth muscle fibers (10) are inserted on the perichondrium (2) of the free ends of the cartilage; they form the trachealis muscle.

The tracheal tube is lined by a mucosa, in the lamina propria (6, 12) of which there are serous (4) and mucous (5) alveoli. Ducts of these glands (11), opening into the lumen of the trachea, are also present. The surface epithelium is pseudostratified columnar ciliated epithelium with goblet cells (14). Along the dorsal wall of the trachea where no underlying cartilage occurs the mucosa is thrown into folds (13).

PLATE 77 (Fig. 2)

TRACHEA (SECTIONAL VIEW)

The perichondrium (1), made up of fibrous connective tissue, is continuous with the connective tissue of the deeper area of the lamina propria, which holds serous, mucous and mixed alveoli (8). There is a pseudostratified columnar ciliated epithelium, with occasional goblet cells (9). The basement membrane is characteristically thickened. See also Plate 5, Fig. 1.

Chondrocytes near the surface of the cartilage are flattened (3) and gradually become similar to the fibrocytes of the perichondrium.

See also Plate 12, Fig. 2.

PLATE 77

TRACHEA

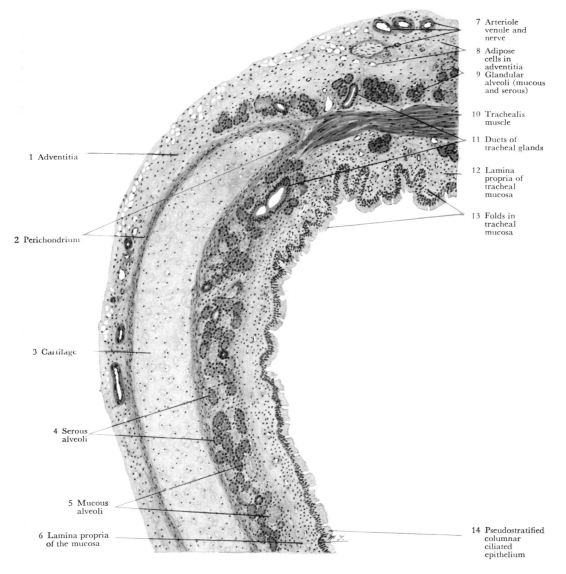

7 Arteriole venule and nerve

8 Adipose cells in adventitia

9 Glandular alveoli (mucous and serous)

10 Trachealis muscle

11 Ducts of tracheal glands

12 Lamina propria of tracheal mucosa

13 Folds in tracheal mucosa

1 Adventitia

2 Perichondrium

3 Cartilage

4 Serous alveoli

5 Mucous alveoli

6 Lamina propria of the mucosa

14 Pseudostratified columnar ciliated epithelium

Fig. 1. — *Trachea (panoramic view, transverse section)*.
Stain: hematoxylin-eosin. 50×.

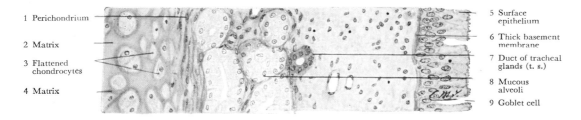

1 Perichondrium

2 Matrix

3 Flattened chondrocytes

4 Matrix

5 Surface epithelium

6 Thick basement membrane

7 Duct of tracheal glands (t. s.)

8 Mucous alveoli

9 Goblet cell

Fig. 2. — *Trachea (sectional view)*.
Stain: hematoxylin-eosin. 220×.

PLATE 78

LUNG (PANORAMIC VIEW)

Terminology has varied for the different divisions of the respiratory tract. The terminology employed here is that in current use, based on the concept of bronchopulmonary segments. From the exterior to the alveolus, the divisions are: primary bronchi, secondary or lobar bronchi, segmental (small or tertiary) bronchi, bronchioles, terminal bronchioles, respiratory bronchioles, alveolar ducts, alveolar sacs, alveoli. The histological characteristics of several of these divisions are shown on Plate 79. The distinguishing features are indicated on this panoramic view of lung tissue.

Structure of the primary bronchi is at first like that of the trachea. When they enter the lung, the C-shaped cartilage is replaced by separate plates of cartilage which encircle the bronchus, and the smooth muscle spreads out from the trachealis muscle to form an incomplete layer around the lumen.

A secondary or lobar bronchus is identified by the closeness of its several cartilage plates (33, and Plate 79, Fig. 1). The lining of the bronchus is pseudostratified columnar ciliated epithelium (32). Making up the wall, one sees, in succession, a thin lamina propria, a narrow layer of smooth muscle (31), a submucosa in which are scattered bronchial glands, hyaline cartilage plates (30), and the adventitia.

Segmental bronchi retain a similar structure, but the epithelium becomes lower, and each of the other elements decreases in amount.

In bronchioles (16), the epithelium is low pseudostratified columnar ciliated or low columnar ciliated, with goblet cells interspersed. The mucosa is typically folded, producing a stellate lumen in cross section. The band of smooth muscle is prominent. Adventitia surrounds this, since glands and cartilage are no longer present.

Each terminal bronchiole (6, 12) has a spacious, irregular lumen, with a wavy epithelial lining when seen in cross-section. The epithelium is ciliated columnar; goblet cells are lacking. Still present are a thin lamina propria, the layer of smooth muscle, and an adventitia.

The respiratory bronchioles (5, 8, 17, 23, 26, 27) are the tubules in direct connection with alveolar ducts and alveoli. The epithelium is low columnar or cuboidal (5, 8); it may be ciliated in the proximal portion. Minimal connective tissue supports the band of intermingled smooth muscle and elastic fibers of the lamina propria, and the accompanying blood vessels. Alveoli appear in the wall, on the side opposite the pulmonary artery (5; 26, left side). These increase in number going distally (5; 26, 23); here epithelium and muscle of the distal respiratory bronchiole are seen as small, intermittent areas between the openings of the numerous alveoli (5, upper leader; 17; 23, 24, 25).

Each distal respiratory bronchiole opens into two or more alveolar ducts, although in sections only one such alveolar duct may be seen (5 and 2, lower leader; 23, upper leader and 22, middle leader). Walls of alveolar ducts are formed by a series of alveoli lying adjacent to each other (2, 15, 22). A group or cluster of alveoli opening into an alveolar duct is an alveolar sac (14, 20).

The alveoli (4, 21, 25) form the mass of the parenchyma of the lung, giving the appearance of fine lace. See Fig. 4, Plate 79, for details.

A fortuitous plane of section shows a continuous passageway from terminal bronchiole into alveolar ducts (6, 5, lowest leader of 2; 26, 23, middle leader of 22).

The pulmonary artery (an elastic artery) branches repeatedly to accompany the divisions of the bronchial tree (7, 10, 28). Larger pulmonary vein branches accompany the bronchi and bronchioles; numerous smaller branches are seen in the trabeculae of the lung (3).

Very small bronchial arteries supply the walls of the various bronchi and bronchioles and included structures (and other areas). Small bronchial veins (29) may be seen in the larger bronchi.

The visceral pleura (1) is composed of a thin layer of connective tissue (19) and a layer of mesothelium (18).

PLATE 78

LUNG (PANORAMIC VIEW)

1 Visceral
  pleura

2 Alveolar
  ducts (l. s.)

3 Trabecula
  with
  pulmonary
  vein

4 Alveolus

5 Respiratory
  bronchiole
  (distal and
  proximal
  portions)
6 Terminale
  bronchiole
7 Pulmonary
  arteriole
8 Respiratory
  bronchiole
  (t. s.)
9 Alveolar
  duct (t. s.)

10 Pulmonary
   arteriole
11 Lymph
   nodule

12 Terminal
   bronchiole

13 Smooth
   muscle

14 Alveolar
   sac

15 Alveolar
   duct (l. s.)
16 Bronchiole

17 Respiratory
   bronchiole
   (distal
   portion, l. s.)

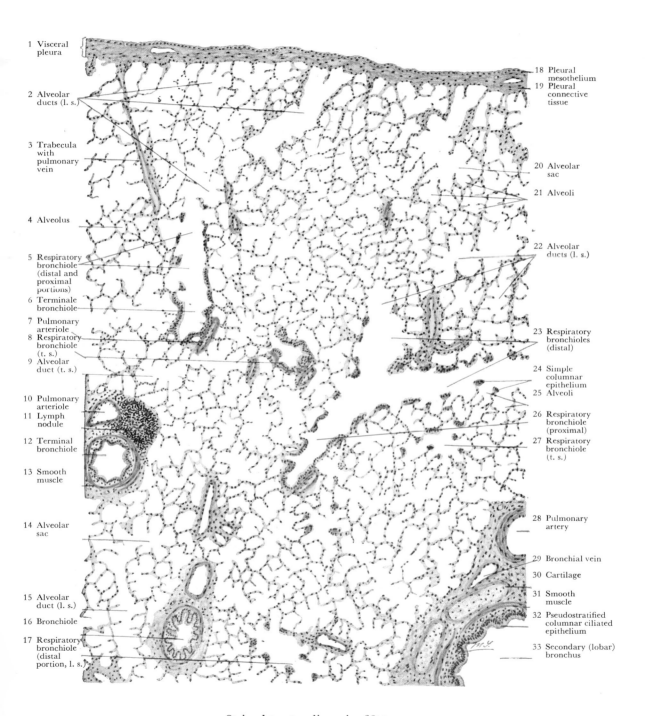

18 Pleural
   mesothelium
19 Pleural
   connective
   tissue

20 Alveolar
   sac

21 Alveoli

22 Alveolar
   ducts (l. s.)

23 Respiratory
   bronchioles
   (distal)

24 Simple
   columnar
   epithelium
25 Alveoli

26 Respiratory
   bronchiole
   (proximal)
27 Respiratory
   bronchiole
   (t. s.)

28 Pulmonary
   artery

29 Bronchial vein

30 Cartilage

31 Smooth
   muscle

32 Pseudostratified
   columnar ciliated
   epithelium

33 Secondary (lobar)
   bronchus

Stain: hematoxylin-eosin. 30×.

PLATE 79 (Fig. 1)

SECONDARY (LOBAR) BRONCHUS

The secondary (lobar) bronchus is lined with pseudostratified columnar ciliated ("respiratory") epithelium (12). This is surrounded by a thin lamina propria (13) of fine fibered connective tissue with many elastic fibers (not illustrated) and scanty lymphoid cells. Ducts (2) of submucosal glands pass through it to open into the lumen. A thin layer of smooth muscle (6) surrounds the lamina propria.

In the submucosa are glands, which may consist of groups of serous alveoli only (5, 8), or groups of serous and mucous alveoli intermingled (10); demilunes may be present.

The several cartilage plates (4) are close together. They will become smaller and farther apart as division of bronchi continues. Between them, connective tissue of the submucosa blends with that of the adventitia (3), which is a well developed layer.

The accompanying branch of the pulmonary artery (15) may be seen in the outer adventitia or adjacent to it. A small branch of the pulmonary artery (7), probably accompanies a small bronchus or bronchiole which is in another plane of section.

Bronchial vessels are seen in the connective tissue of the bronchus: an arteriole (16), a venule (11), and capillaries (9).

(Fig. 2)

BRONCHIOLE

A bronchiole is of small diameter, about 1 mm., with a stellate lumen. The lining epithelium is low pseudostratified columnar ciliated or columnar ciliated, with goblet cells. A well developed smooth muscle layer (3) surrounds a thin lamina propria, and is in turn surrounded by the adventitia (2). Cartilage and glands are lacking.

Adjacent to the bronchiole is a branch of the pulmonary artery (6). The bronchiole is surrounded by parenchyma (alveoli) of the lung (1).

(Fig. 3)

RESPIRATORY BRONCHIOLE

A respiratory bronchiole and associated structures are illustrated. The wall of the bronchiole (4) is lined with cuboidal epithelium; cilia and goblet cells are lacking. Smooth muscle fibers (3) are seen adjacent to the epithelium. Neighboring alveoli (1) and a satellite branch of the pulmonary artery (5) are shown. "Alveolization" of the bronchiole occurs on the side opposite the artery.

(Fig. 4)

ALVEOLAR WALL

The relationship of alveoli to capillaries is illustrated. Capillaries with erythrocytes (1) can be seen in the alveolar walls (4). The capillaries are formed by endothelial cells and surrounded by adventitial cells (6). The free ends of the alveolar septa forming the mouth of an alveolus are slightly thickened by a ring of smooth muscle fibers (2). An epithelial lining of the alveoli is not discernible under the magnification used, but electron microscopy has established that a fine one does exist.

PLATE 79

LUNG

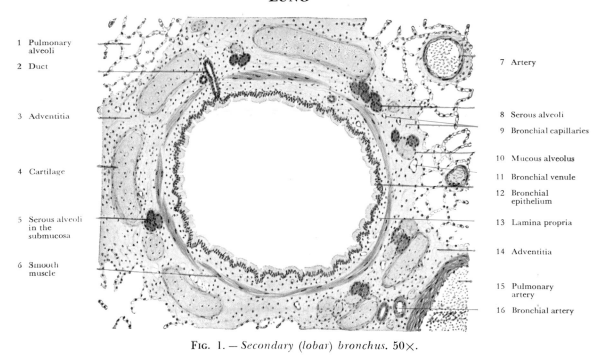

1 Pulmonary
  alveoli

2 Duct

3 Adventitia

4 Cartilage

5 Serous alveoli
  in the
  submucosa

6 Smooth
  muscle

7 Artery

8 Serous alveoli

9 Bronchial capillaries

10 Mucous alveolus

11 Bronchial venule

12 Bronchial
   epithelium

13 Lamina propria

14 Adventitia

15 Pulmonary
   artery

16 Bronchial artery

FIG. 1. — *Secondary (lobar) bronchus.* 50×.

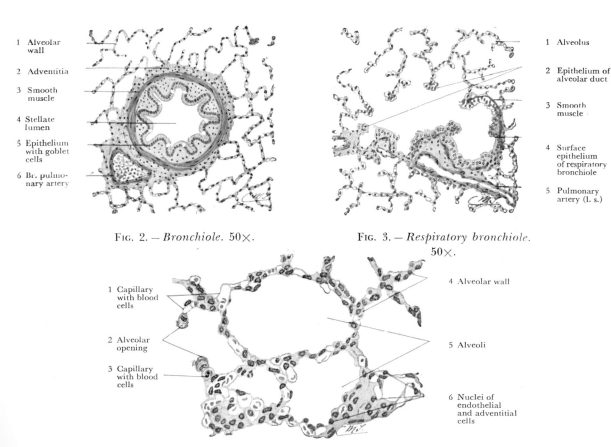

1 Alveolar
  wall

2 Adventitia

3 Smooth
  muscle

4 Stellate
  lumen

5 Epithelium
  with goblet
  cells

6 Br. pulmo-
  nary artery

1 Alveolus

2 Epithelium of
  alveolar duct

3 Smooth
  muscle

4 Surface
  epithelium
  of respiratory
  bronchiole

5 Pulmonary
  artery (l. s.)

FIG. 2. — *Bronchiole.* 50×.

FIG. 3. — *Respiratory bronchiole.*
50×.

1 Capillary
  with blood
  cells

2 Alveolar
  opening

3 Capillary
  with blood
  cells

4 Alveolar wall

5 Alveoli

6 Nuclei of
  endothelial
  and adventitial
  cells

FIG. 4. — *Alveolar wall.* 700×. Stain: hematoxylin-eosin.

PLATE 80

KIDNEY: ONE PYRAMID AND ADJACENT CORTEX
(PANORAMIC VIEW)

The substance of the kidney is divided into cortex (19) and medulla (20).

The cortex, stained deep pink in the sections shown, contains the glomeruli (2, 8) and sections through the proximal and distal convoluted tubules (3) and the upper portions of the loops of Henle. The cortex corticis (1) is that part of the cortex which lies between the peripheral ends of the medullary rays (5) and the outer surface of the kidney.

The medulla is composed of eight to eighteen (an average of twelve) cones, termed renal pyramids or pyramids of Malpighi. Each pyramid lies with the base directed toward the periphery of the kidney and the apex directed inward. The apices of two or more pyramids coalesce to form a renal papilla (15) projecting into one of the minor calyces (13) of the kidney. Cuboidal epithelium (12) usually covers each renal papilla. As this epithelium recurves to the outer wall of the calyx, it becomes transitional epithelium. Collecting tubules form the major substance of each renal pyramid. These tubules coalesce as they reach the summit of a papilla and open into the surrounding minor calyx through fifteen or twenty minute pores. Minor calyces are outward extensions of the two (or more) major calyces, which in turn are extensions of the renal pelvis. Outward extensions of the medulla subdivide the cortex; these extensions are termed medullary rays (5), cortical rays, or pyramids of Ferrein (not to be confused with pyramids of Malpighi of which they are a part). Those parts of the cortex between the medullary rays are termed cortical labyrinths or pars convoluta, and contain glomeruli, proximal and distal convoluted tubules, and interlobular arteries and veins and their subdivisions.

In the connective tissue (16) located near the hilus of the kidney lie numerous blood vessels, which are large branches of the renal artery and vein (14). Other smaller branches penetrate the parenchyma; these are the interlobar (10), the arciform (arcuate) (9), and interlobular (6, 7) blood vessels.

A fibrous capsule (18) surrounds the kidney, which lies embedded in adipose tissue (17) or perirenal fat.

PLATE 80

KIDNEY: ONE PYRAMID AND ADJACENT CORTEX
(PANORAMIC VIEW)

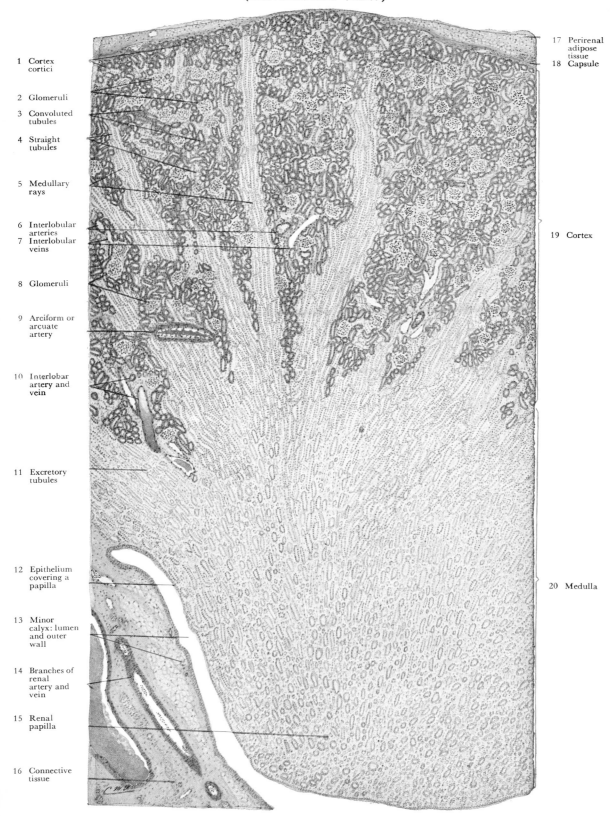

1 Cortex cortici

2 Glomeruli

3 Convoluted tubules

4 Straight tubules

5 Medullary rays

6 Interlobular arteries
7 Interlobular veins

8 Glomeruli

9 Arciform or arcuate artery

10 Interlobar artery and vein

11 Excretory tubules

12 Epithelium covering a papilla

13 Minor calyx: lumen and outer wall

14 Branches of renal artery and vein

15 Renal papilla

16 Connective tissue

17 Perirenal adipose tissue
18 Capsule

19 Cortex

20 Medulla

Stain: hematoxylin-eosin. 25×.

PLATE 81

KIDNEY: DEEP CORTICAL AREA

The conspicuous circular areas are renal (Malpighian) corpuscles. Each is composed of a glomerulus (3), surrounded by a Bowman's capsule (2). The glomerulus is a twisted mass of branching capillaries surrounded by epithelial cells and a few connective tissue cells. Erythrocytes may be seen in the capillaries. An afferent arteriole (15) enters each glomerulus to give rise to the capillaries. Bowman's capsule is composed of an outer parietal epithelium, or capsular epithelium (16) and an inner visceral epithelium, or glomerular epithelium (16). Fluid gathered in Bowman's capsule is drained by way of a uriniferous tubule (8).

Numerous tubules, cut in various planes, lie in the area adjacent to the glomeruli. These tubules stain heavily with eosin and are of two types: proximal convoluted tubules (4, 9, 14, 20) and distal convoluted tubules (1, 13). The proximal convoluted tubules are more numerous, have a relatively small lumen, and are composed of large, broad cuboidal cells with a brush border. The distal convoluted tubules are fewer in number, have a larger lumen, and smaller more distinctly cuboidal cells without a brush border.

Farther removed from the glomeruli lie other tubules, cut, for the most part, longitudinally. These tubules are the upper parts of the collecting tubules (5, 18). In them the lumen is conspicuous, the cuboidal cells stain lightly with eosin, cell membranes are distinct. These tubules are more numerous in the lower part of the picture (11, 12) in the transitional area between cortex and medulla. In this area are also found the narrow descending (12, 22) and thicker ascending (10, 19) divisions of Henle's loops.

PLATE 81

KIDNEY: DEEP CORTICAL AREA

1 Distal convoluted tubules

2 Bowman's capsule, epithelial lining

3 Glomerulus

4 Proximal convoluted tubules

5 Collecting tubules

6 Interlobular vein

7 Glomerular arteriole (t. s.)

8 Junction of a uriniferous tubule with Bowman's capsule

9 Proximal convoluted tubules

10 Ascending branch of Henle's loop

11 Collecting tubules

12 Descending branch of Henle's loop

13 Distal convoluted tubules

14 Proximal convoluted tubules with brush border

15 Glomerular arteriole (l. s.)

16 Visceral and parietal layers of Bowman's capsule

17 Interlobular artery sectioned obliquely, wall and lumen

18 Collecting tubules

19 Ascending branch of Henle's loop

20 Proximal and distal convoluted tubules

21 Collecting tubules

22 Narrow descending branch of Henle's loop

23 Capillaries

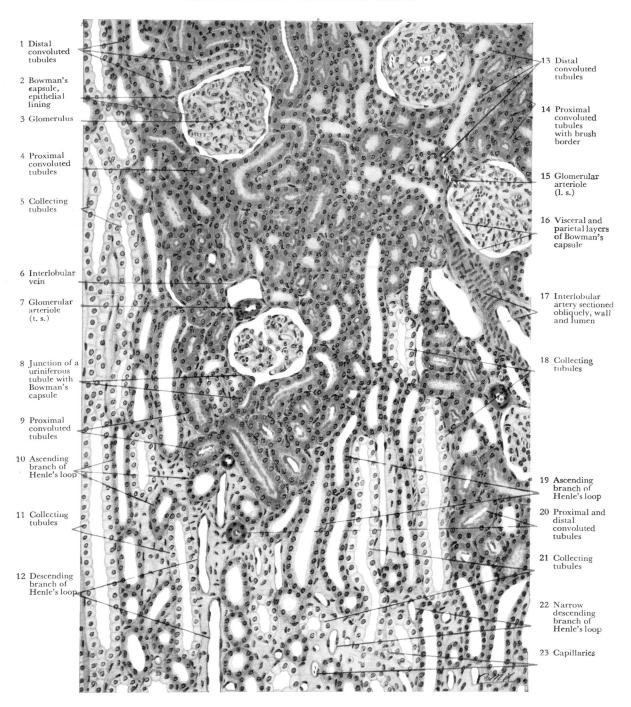

Stain: hematoxylin-eosin. 150×.

PLATE 82 (Fig. 1)

KIDNEY: MEDULLA (PAPILLA), TRANSVERSE SECTION

The final collecting tubules, the papillary ducts (2, 6), are of large diameter, have wide lumens, and are lined by tall, clear columnar cells. There are several cross sections of narrow descending branches of Henle's loop (3, 8) and a few of the thicker ascending branches (1, 7). Connective tissue (10) is more abundant than elsewhere in the kidney. Numerous capillaries (4, 9) are present.

PLATE 82 (Fig. 2)

KIDNEY: PAPILLA ADJACENT TO A CALYX
(SECTIONAL VIEW)

Large collecting tubules, the papillary ducts (5), are seen near their openings at the tip of the papilla. The papilla, in this illustration, is covered by a stratified cuboidal epithelium (8). However, at the actual area cribosa, the covering epithelium is usually simple columnar, a continuation of that lining the papillary ducts. Numerous narrow descending branches of Henle's loop (3, 4, 6) and a few of the thicker ascending branches (1) can be identified. Abundant connective tissue (7) and many capillaries (2) are present.

PLATE 82

KIDNEY: MEDULLA (PAPILLA)

1 Ascending branch of Henle's loop

2 Papillary ducts (terminal collecting tubule), (t. s.)

3 Descending branches of Henle's loop

4 Capillaries

5 Papillary ducts (terminal collecting tubules)

6 Papillary ducts

7 Ascending branch of Henle's loop

8 Descending branch of Henle's loop

9 Capillaries

10 Connective tissue

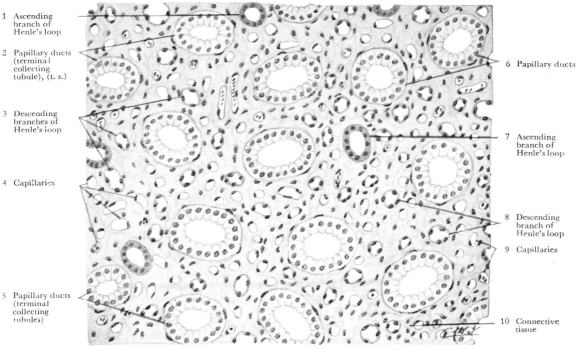

FIG. 1. — *Transverse section.*
Stain: hematoxylin-eosin. 170x

KIDNEY: PAPILLA

1 Ascending branch of Henle's loop

2 Capillary

3 Descending branch of Henle's loop

4 Descending branch of Henle's loop (t. s.)

5 Papillary ducts (l. s.)

6 Descending branch of Henle's loop

7 Connective tissue.

8 Epithelium covering the papilla

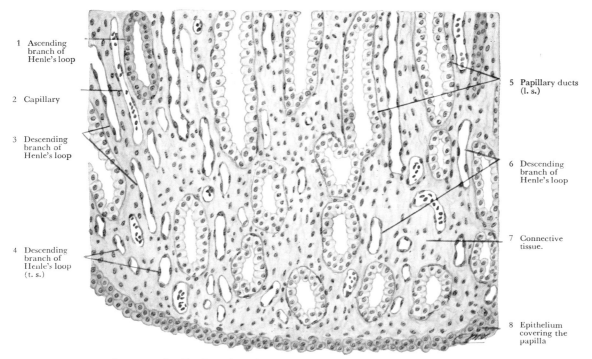

FIG. 2. — *Longitudinal section through an area adjacent to a calyx.*
Stain: hematoxylin-eosin. 120×.

PLATE 83 (Fig. 1)

URETER (TRANSVERSE SECTION)

The duct has a star-shaped lumen, lined by a mucosa composed of transitional epithelium (10), the superficial layer of which shows a narrow acidophilic band (9); and a wide lamina propria (5), of connective tissue which is dense adjacent to the epithelium, but relatively loose (5) near the muscular coat.

The muscular coat is made up of an inner longitudinal layer (3) and an outer circular layer (2).

The adventitia (6) contains numerous adipose cells (1, 12) and blood vessels (8), and a few nerves (7).

PLATE 83 (Fig. 2)

URETER: A SECTOR OF THE WALL

Higher magnification shows the structure of the different coats in greater detail. The outer cell layer of the epithelium (8) is more darkly staining than the deeper layers, and shows the superficial cuticle (9) which renders the cells impermeable to urine.

The lamina propria (12) forms no papillae beneath the epithelium. The spindle shape (7) and central nucleus (11) of the smooth muscle fibers are clearly visible.

In the adventitia (5) lie adipose cells (6) and several blood vessels: capillaries (4), an arteriole (2), and venules 1, 3).

See also Plate 5, Fig. 2.

PLATE 83

URETER

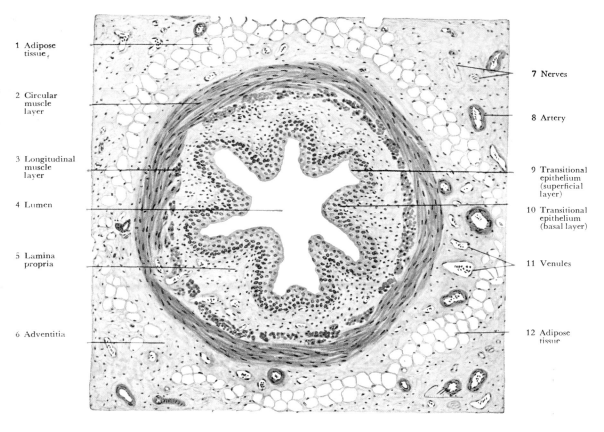

1 Adipose tissue

2 Circular muscle layer

3 Longitudinal muscle layer

4 Lumen

5 Lamina propria

6 Adventitia

7 Nerves

8 Artery

9 Transitional epithelium (superficial layer)

10 Transitional epithelium (basal layer)

11 Venules

12 Adipose tissue

FIG. 1. — *Transverse section.*
Stain: hematoxylin-eosin. 50×.

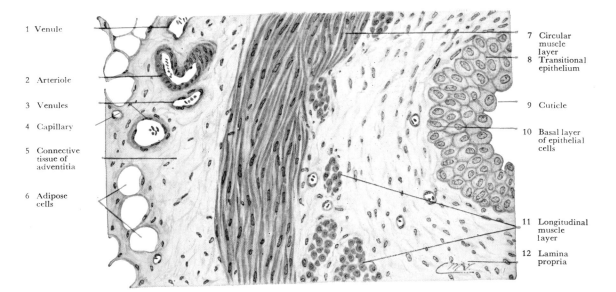

1 Venule

2 Arteriole

3 Venules

4 Capillary

5 Connective tissue of adventitia

6 Adipose cells

7 Circular muscle layer

8 Transitional epithelium

9 Cuticle

10 Basal layer of epithelial cells

11 Longitudinal muscle layer

12 Lamina propria

FIG. 2. — *A sector of the wall.*
Stain: hematoxylin-eosin. 150×.

PLATE 84 (Fig. 1)

URINARY BLADDER, UPPER PART: WALL

A thick, plexiform muscular coat (1, 10) is the outstanding feature of the wall of the bladder. The outer surface of the wall is composed of connective tissue (4) covered by mesothelium (5). Its inner surface is lined by a mucosa with many folds (6). The lamina propria (9) is continuous with the connective tissue of the muscular coat (2); it does not form subepithelial papillae. A submucosa is not usually distinguishable.

The epithelium is of the transitional type (8). See also Plate 5, Fig. 2.

The lower part of the urinary bladder is covered by adventitia, which attaches it to surrounding structures.

PLATE 84 (Fig. 2)

URINARY BLADDER: MUCOSA

To the left are shown smooth muscle fibers cut transversally (1), and interfascicular connective tissue continuous with the lamina propria of the mucosa (2). Numerous blood vessels are found in the lamina propria; those deeply situated are larger than those near the epithelium (3, 4, 7).

The epithelium is of the transitional type, composed of similar cells except for those at the surface which are more markedly acidophilic and have an outer cuticle. The cells are rounded, or somewhat columnar or cuboidal, in the contracted parts of the mucosa (5); the surface cells tend to be larger than the deeper ones (6). In the distended areas, the epithelium is thinner, and the surface cells become more elongated like broad squamous cells (8).

PLATE 84

URINARY BLADDER (UPPER PART)

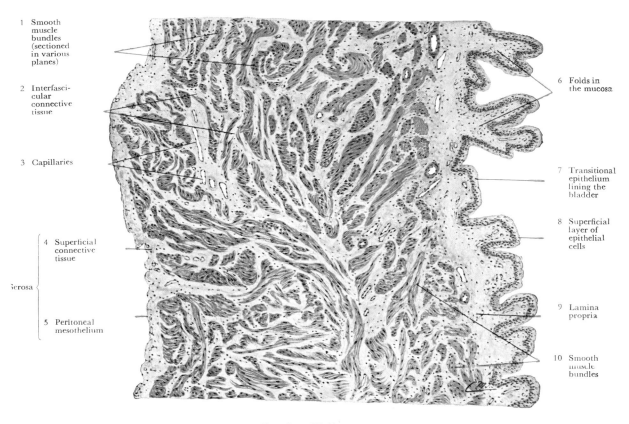

1 Smooth muscle bundles (sectioned in various planes)

2 Interfascicular connective tissue

3 Capillaries

4 Superficial connective tissue

Serosa

5 Peritoneal mesothelium

6 Folds in the mucosa

7 Transitional epithelium lining the bladder

8 Superficial layer of epithelial cells

9 Lamina propria

10 Smooth muscle bundles

FIG. 1. — *Wall.*
Stain: hematoxylin-eosin. 40×.

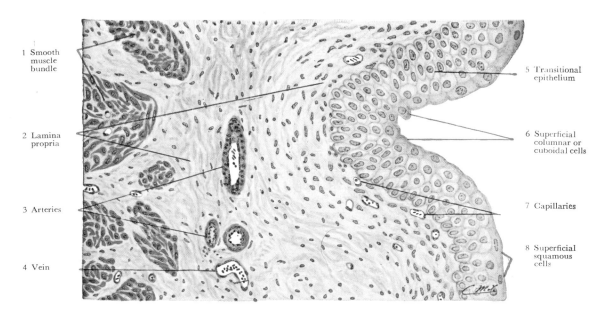

1 Smooth muscle bundle

2 Lamina propria

3 Arteries

4 Vein

5 Transitional epithelium

6 Superficial columnar or cuboidal cells

7 Capillaries

8 Superficial squamous cells

FIG. 2. — *Mucosa.*
Stain: hematoxylin-eosin. 160×.

PLATE 85 (Fig. 1)

HYPOPHYSIS (PITUITARY GLAND): PANORAMIC VIEW, SAGITTAL SECTION

There are four divisions of the hypophysis: pars distalis (5); pars nervosa (11); the pars intermedia (10); and the pars tuberalis (9), which enfolds the stalk like a sheath and is hence seen above and below the stalk in a sagittal section. All four parts of the gland are enclosed by a capsule of connective tissue (2) in which numerous blood vessels lie (7).

The pars distalis (5) is the largest of the four divisions; it is also termed the anterior lobe. Its glandular substance is composed of two main varieties of cells: chromophobe cells (1) and chromophile cells (3, 4). The former are also known as the principal cells. The latter are further classified as alpha (acidophilic) cells (3) and beta (basophilic) cells (4). (See Fig. 2, below).

The pars nervosa (11) is the second largest of the four divisions. Together with the pars intermedia it forms the posterior lobe of the pituitary. It stains light blue and is predominantly fibrillar in structure. Numerous bands of connective tissue (12) arising from the capsule, penetrate into its substance.

The pars intermedia (10) lies between the pars distalis and the pars nervosa. In it are vesicles filled with colloid. Basophilic cell groups predominate in this division of the pituitary.

The pars tuberalis (9) surrounds the infundibulum like a sheath, rising higher on the anterior than on the posterior aspect. The pituitary is joined to the base of the brain by the infundibular stalk (8).

The pars nervosa, or infundibular process, is part of the larger unit, the neurohypophysis, which includes also the tuber cinereum of the median eminence and the infundibular stalk. The adenohypophysis includes the cellular portions derived from oral ectoderm: the pars distalis (5), pars intermedia (10), and pars tuberalis (9).

PLATE 85 (Fig. 2)

HYPOPHYSIS (PITUITARY GLAND): SECTIONAL VIEW

Under higher magnification, cells of the pars distalis may be distinguished. Chromophobe cells (4) have a homogenous cytoplasm and stain lightly; typically they are smaller than chromophile cells and hence in groups their nuclei are closer together. Chromophile cells stain well: either red, acidophilic (alpha) cells (3); or violet, basophilic (beta) cells (5).

Numerous sinusoids (6) are in evidence in the pars distalis, lined by reticuloendothelial cells (1).

The vesicles (7) of the pars intermedia are filled with colloid and lined with low columnar epithelial cells, with or without basophilic granules in the cytoplasm. In the neighborhood of the vesicles are follicles of basophilic cells (8).

The pars nervosa (infundibular process) lies to the right. It is recognized by the presence of nerve fibers (9), among which are numerous nuclei of modified glial cells, the pituicytes (10).

PLATE 85

HYPOPHYSIS (PITUITARY GLAND)

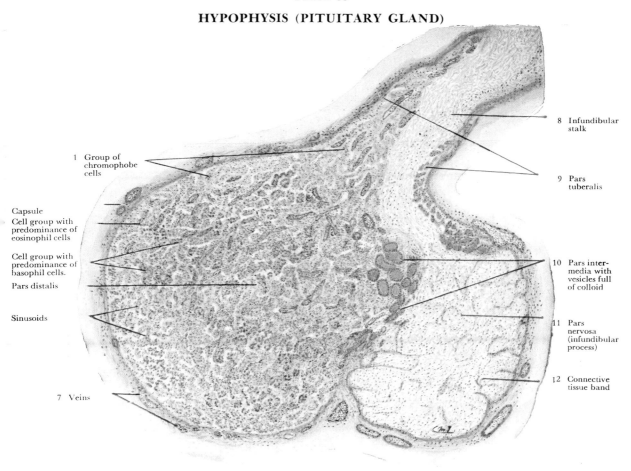

1 Group of chromophobe cells

Capsule

Cell group with predominance of eosinophil cells

Cell group with predominance of basophil cells.

Pars distalis

Sinusoids

7 Veins

8 Infundibular stalk

9 Pars tuberalis

10 Pars intermedia with vesicles full of colloid

11 Pars nervosa (infundibular process)

12 Connective tissue band

FIG. 1. — *Panoramic view (sagittal section)*.
Stain: hematoxylin-eosin. 22×.

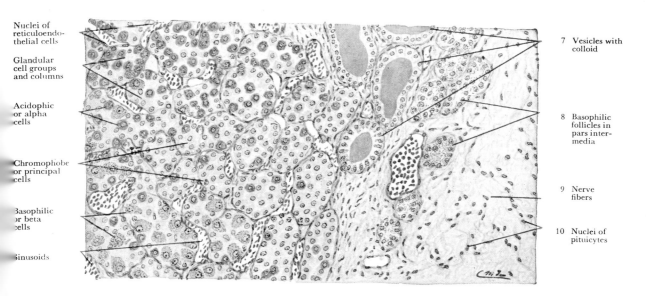

Nuclei of reticuloendothelial cells

Glandular cell groups and columns

Acidophic or alpha cells

Chromophobe or principal cells

Basophilic or beta cells

Sinusoids

7 Vesicles with colloid

8 Basophilic follicles in pars intermedia

9 Nerve fibers

10 Nuclei of pituicytes

FIG. 2. — *Sectional view*.
Stain: hematoxylin-eosin. 200×.

PLATE 86 (Fig. 1)

HYPOPHYSIS: PARS DISTALIS (AZAN STAIN)

Corrosive sublimate mixtures are used as fixatives. The section is then stained with azocarmine and differentiated with aniline oil. Phosphotungstic acid is then used to destain the connective tissue, followed by Aniline blue and Orange G as stains. Nuclei stain orange; collagenous and reticular fibers stain blue; erythrocytes stain bright red; and protoplasmic granules stain red, orange or blue according to their respective affinities. Thus the cell types in the pars distalis are readily identified.

Chromophobes (3) stain lightly, as after any stain. Nuclei are pale, cytoplasm is a pale orange, cell outlines are not defined. Their frequent arrangement in groups or clumps is evident.

The two types of acidophils can be distinguished by their staining reaction: the carminophils or epsilon acidophils (1), whose granules stain with azocarmine, and the orangeophils or alpha acidophils (6), whose granules stain mainly with Orange G.

Basophils (beta cells) are readily recognizable by the blue staining of their granules (2, 5). The different types of basophils are not distinguishable, but it is seen that the degree of granularity, and therefore the density of the stain, varies in different cells.

PLATE 86 (Fig. 2)

HYPOPHYSIS: CELL GROUPS (AZAN STAIN)

Typical cells of the hypophysis, stained with Azan as in Fig. 1, are shown here at a higher magnification.

Nuclei of all cells are stained reddish-orange.

In chromophobes (a), the light orange stain emphasizes the cell characteristics: the non-granular cytoplasm and the vague cell boundaries.

In the rounded or oval alpha acidophils (b), the heavy granules in the cytoplasm take an intense orange stain. Cell outlines are clearly defined. These cells lie in close proximity to a sinusoid.

The basophils shown here (c) have an angular shape; others may be rounded or oval. Their blue granules are not as compactly arranged as are alpha cell granules.

At (d) are pituicytes from the pars nervosa. Here we see nuclei and cells of different shapes and sizes. The small amount of cytoplasm, stained light orange, sends out diffuse processes for varying distances.

PLATE 86

FIG. 1. HYPOPHYSIS: PARS DISTALIS (AZAN STAIN)

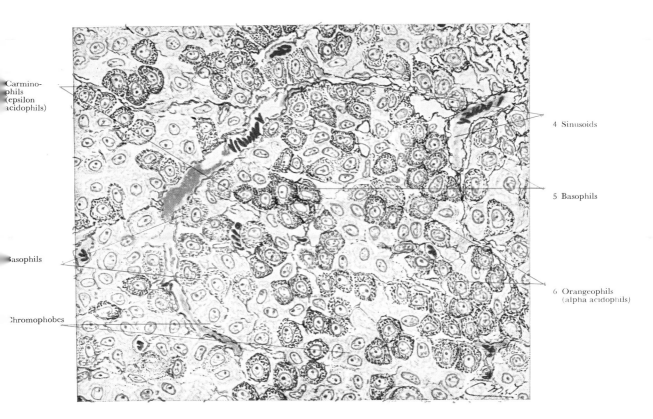

Carmino-phils (epsilon acidophils)

4 Sinusoids

5 Basophils

Basophils

6 Orangeophils (alpha acidophils)

Chromophobes

Sectional view. Nuclei: orange; cytoplasmic granules of alpha cells: red or orange; cytoplasmic granules of beta cells: deep blue; collagenous and reticular fibers: blue; erythrocytes: bright red; hemolyzed blood: deep yellow. About 500×.

FIG. 2. HYPOPHYSIS: CELL GROUPS (AZAN STAIN) 800×

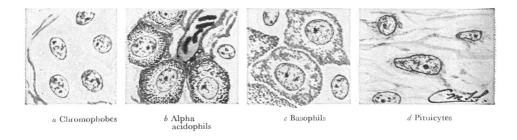

a Chromophobes   b Alpha acidophils   c Basophils   d Pituicytes

— 185 —

Plate 87

THYROID GLAND

The thyroid is composed of vesicles, or follicles (3, 4), lined by columnar or cuboidal epithelium with round nuclei (6). These vesicles are filled with colloid stained by eosin. The colloid (1) shrinks in some cases from the vesicular wall, owing to the reagents used. Prominent bands of connective tissue (5) arise from the capsule enclosing the thyroid and penetrate the body of the gland, dividing it into groups of follicles. Relatively little connective tissue is found between the follicles of a group.

Some of the follicles have been cut tangentially (4), giving the appearance of solid structures.

PLATE 87

THYROID GLAND

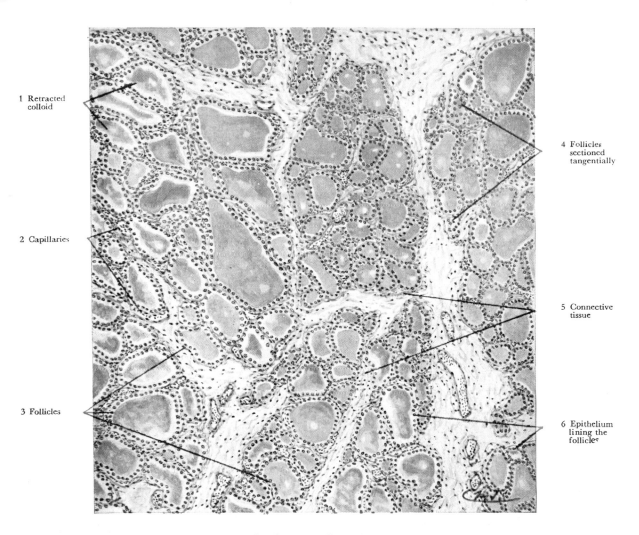

1 Retracted
colloid

2 Capillaries

3 Follicles

4 Follicles
sectioned
tangentially

5 Connective
tissue

6 Epithelium
lining the
follicles

Stain: hematoxylin-eosin. 90×.

PLATE 88 (Fig. 1)

THYROID GLAND (SECTIONAL VIEW)

The follicles are lined by epithelium, the cells being flattened (1) in some cases, cuboidal or low columnar (2) in others. Colloid (4) fills the follicular cavity and in some cases appears retracted or vacuolized (6). A group of cells (7), placed between the follicles is a follicular wall cut tangentially.

Capillaries (3) and fibrillar connective tissue (5) lie between the follicles.

PLATE 88 (Fig. 2)

PARATHYROID GLAND

Parathyroid tissue in the adult human is composed of two principal types of cells: principal or chief cells (7) and oxyphilic cells (3). The principal cells are by far the more numerous; usually they appear in masses or columns and are not separated into distinct lobules by connective tissue, as is thyroid tissue. Oxyphilic (acidophilic) cells (3, 6) occur singly or in groups. They are larger than the principal cells, cytoplasm is granular and acidophilic, nuclei are more darkly stained. In man, transitional cells between oxyphilic and principal types are common. Oxyphilic cells, however, are not normally present in children.

Spaces (2), filled with colloid, occasionally occur among the cells. The tissue is well supplied with blood vessels (4).

PLATE 88

THYROID AND PARATHYROID GLANDS

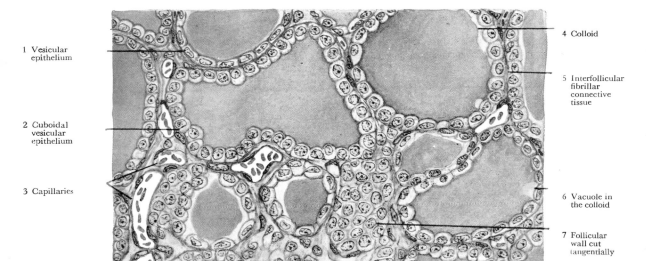

1 Vesicular
  epithelium

2 Cuboidal
  vesicular
  epithelium

3 Capillaries

4 Colloid

5 Interfollicular
  fibrillar
  connective
  tissue

6 Vacuole in
  the colloid

7 Follicular
  wall cut
  tangentially

FIG. 1. — *Thyroid gland (sectional view)*.
Stain: hematoxylin-eosin. 550×.

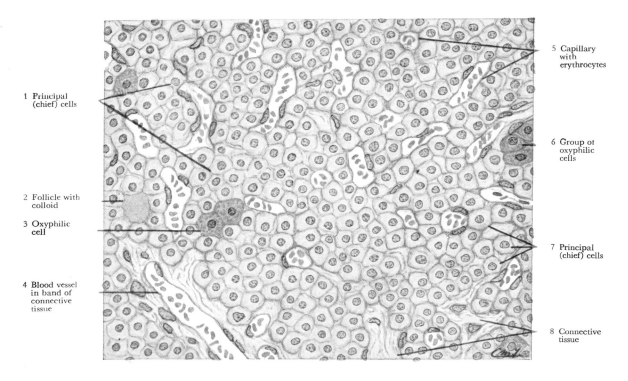

1 Principal
  (chief) cells

2 Follicle with
  colloid

3 Oxyphilic
  cell

4 Blood vessel
  in band of
  connective
  tissue

5 Capillary
  with
  erythrocytes

6 Group of
  oxyphilic
  cells

7 Principal
  (chief) cells

8 Connective
  tissue

FIG. 2. — *Parathyroid gland*.
Stain: hematoxylin-eosin. 550×.

PLATE 89

ADRENAL GLANDS

Each adrenal gland is divided into a cortex (2) and medulla (3).

In the cortex three zones, which may grade into one another, occur. The zona glomerulosa (2a) is the outer zone of the cortex. The nuclei of the cells (6) tend to be small and stain relatively dark. The cytoplasm contains lipoid droplets, which appear as vacuoles in H&E preparations. Cells of the zona fasciculata (2b) appear to lie in columns; because their vacuolization is so marked, they are called spongiocytes. The intervening capillaries (9) are arranged, more or less, in a rectilinear fashion. Cells of the zona reticularis (2c) form cords which run in various directions and anastomose with one another. The cells are frequently loaded with yellow pigment (11). The intervening sinusoids are irregularly arranged.

Cells which make up the major portion of the medulla (3, 14) have relatively clear cytoplasm and tend to lie in clumps. Fresh tissue, when fixed with potassium bichromate, displays fine brown granules; this is called the chromaffin reaction and probably indicates the presence of epinephrine or a closely related substance. The medulla also contains sympathetic ganglion cells (13), placed singly or in groups. In them the nucleus has a vesicular aspect with little chromatin placed peripherally and with a centrally placed dark nucleolus.

Each adrenal gland is encased in a capsule of connective tissue (1). Septa of connective tissue (4) penetrate radially from the capsule into the substance of the gland. Blood vessels and bundles of unmyelinated nerve fibers (5) may be seen in the connective tissue.

PLATE 89

ADRENAL GLANDS

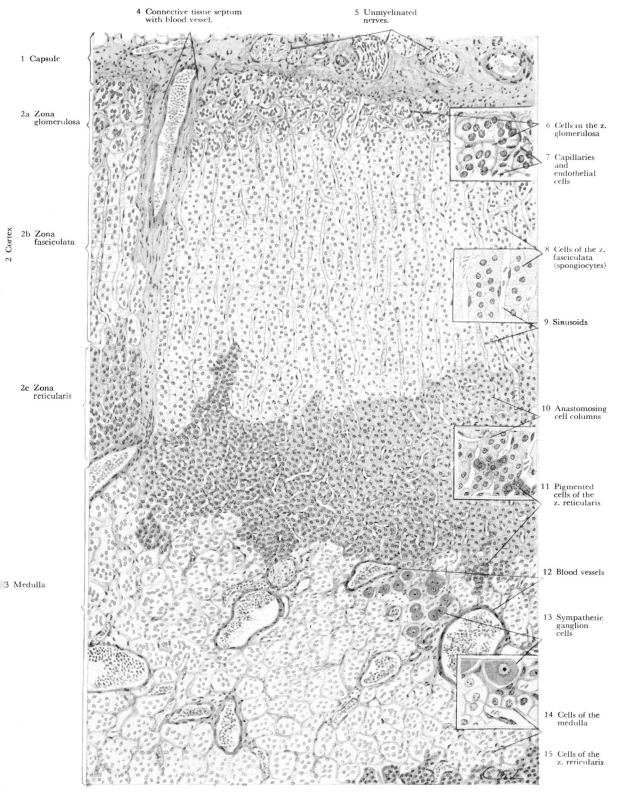

4 Connective tissue septum with blood vessel.

5 Unmyelinated nerves.

1 Capsule

2a Zona glomerulosa

2 Cortex

2b Zona fasciculata

2c Zona reticularis

3 Medulla

6 Cells in the z. glomerulosa

7 Capillaries and endothelial cells

8 Cells of the z. fasciculata (spongiocytes)

9 Sinusoids

10 Anastomosing cell columns

11 Pigmented cells of the z. reticularis

12 Blood vessels

13 Sympathetic ganglion cells

14 Cells of the medulla

15 Cells of the z. reticularis

Stain: hematoxylin-eosin. 200×.

PLATE 90 (Fig. 1)

TESTIS

The seminiferous tubules (2, 3, 8) are lined by several rows of specialized epithelial cells resting on a thin basement membrane (4). The area between the tubules is filled by connective tissue (6) liberally supplied by small blood vessels (9). In this connective tissue are groups of epithelioid cells, the interstitial cells of Leydig (7). The entire testicle is enclosed in a thick fibrous capsule of connective tissue (1), the tunica albuginea.

PLATE 90 (Fig. 2)

DUCTUS EPIDIDYMIDIS (DUCT OF THE EPIDIDYMIS)

The cross sections of the ductus (2) are lined with pseudostratified epithelium (4, 9), composed of ciliated columnar cells (9) and a few rounded basal cells (10). A basement membrane (3) is present. In the lumen of many of the sections are clumps of spermatozoa.

A thin layer of circular smooth muscle fibers (7) surrounds each cross section. The entire ductule is embedded in connective tissue (1), in which blood vessels are found.

At a U-shaped bend in the ductus, the wall has been cut tangentially (6) and appears as a solid sheet of epithelial cells.

The cilia are long, non-motile processes (stereocilia). Secretion from the columnar cells reaches the lumen of the ductus by passing along the stereocilia.

PLATE 90 (Fig. 1)

TESTIS

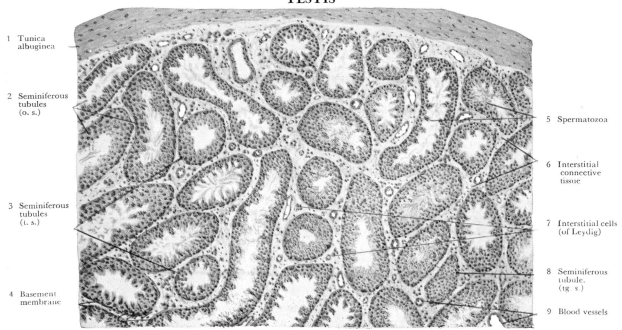

1 Tunica albuginea

2 Seminiferous tubules (o. s.)

3 Seminiferous tubules (l. s.)

4 Basement membrane

5 Spermatozoa

6 Interstitial connective tissue

7 Interstitial cells (of Leydig)

8 Seminiferous tubule. (tg. s.)

9 Blood vessels

Stain: hematoxylin-eosin. 70×.

PLATE 90 (Fig. 2)

DUCTUS EPIDIDYMIDIS (DUCT OF THE EPIDIDYMIS)

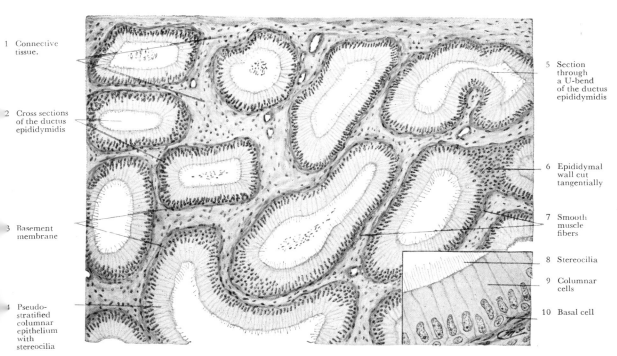

1 Connective tissue.

2 Cross sections of the ductus epididymidis

3 Basement membrane

4 Pseudo-stratified columnar epithelium with stereocilia

5 Section through a U-bend of the ductus epididymidis

6 Epididymal wall cut tangentially

7 Smooth muscle fibers

8 Stereocilia

9 Columnar cells

10 Basal cell

Stain: hematoxylin-eosin. 90×.

PLATE 91

TESTIS: SEMINIFEROUS TUBULES
(TRANSVERSE SECTION)

Sections of several seminiferous tubules are shown. Between the tubules is the interstitial (intertubular) connective tissue which contains fibroblasts (2) and other characteristic cells, blood vessels (4, 12, 25), nerves, and lymphatics. Also present are the specific interstitial cells (of Leydig) which occur typically in groups (3) but may also be seen singly. They are large, rounded or polygonal cells with granular cytoplasm and a distinct ovoid or wrinkled nucleus (34). They constitute the endocrine gland of the testis and produce testosterone.

Each seminiferous tubule is surrounded by an outer lamina propria of compact connective tissue with flattened fibroblasts and an inner, thin, basement membrane (6). Enclosed by the membrane is the complex seminiferous epithelium consisting of two kinds of cells, the supporting cells of Sertoli and the spermatogenic cells. The characteristic arrangement of these cells is seen best in a transverse section of a seminiferous tubule (5).

The supporting Sertoli cells are slender, elongated cells with irregular outlines extending from the basement membrane to the lumen (19, 27). The cytoplasm often exhibits faint longitudinal striations. The distinctive nucleus is ovoid or somewhat triangular in shape, clearly outlined, pale-staining with fine, sparse chromatin, and contains one or more prominent nucleoli. Nuclei may vary in position in different cells. In tangential sections of seminiferous tubules (15), Sertoli cells are seen as ovoid rounded cross sections (16).

Spermatogenic cells are arranged in rows between and around Sertoli cells; in sections, they often appear superimposed on Sertoli cells, obscuring their cytoplasm in varying degrees (8, 13). The most primitive spermatogenic cells, the spermatogonia, lie beneath the basement membrane (17, 18). They are rounded cells with a spherical nucleus containing darkly-staining flakes of chromatin (28). These divide to produce more spermatogonia (1, 21). After a period of growth, some differentiate to larger, primary spermatocytes which lie adjacent to the spermatogonia but nearer the lumen (22, 29). Their nuclei have a variable appearance due to the different states of activity of the chromatin (11, 22). Division stages are prevalent (7). By meiotic division (first maturation division) each primary spermatocyte gives rise to two secondary spermatocytes.

Secondary spermatocytes are smaller than primary spermatocytes and the nuclear chromatin is less dense (23, 30). They divide soon after formation and therefore are not seen frequently in stained testicular tissue. This is the second maturation division, whereby each secondary spermatocyte gives rise to two spermatids. Spermatids are much smaller cells (31) lying usually in groups close to the lumen of the seminiferous tubule (24). They become closely associated with Sertoli cells, and here undergo metamorphosis to form spermatozoa (26, 32-33, 9). The small, deeply-staining heads of spermatozoa appear to be embedded in the cytoplasm of Sertoli cells, their tails hanging into the lumen of the seminiferous tubule (20). Debris from degenerating spermatogenic cells is often seen in the vicinity of spermatozoa (10).

PLATE 91

TESTIS: SEMINIFEROUS TUBULES (TRANSVERSE SECTION)

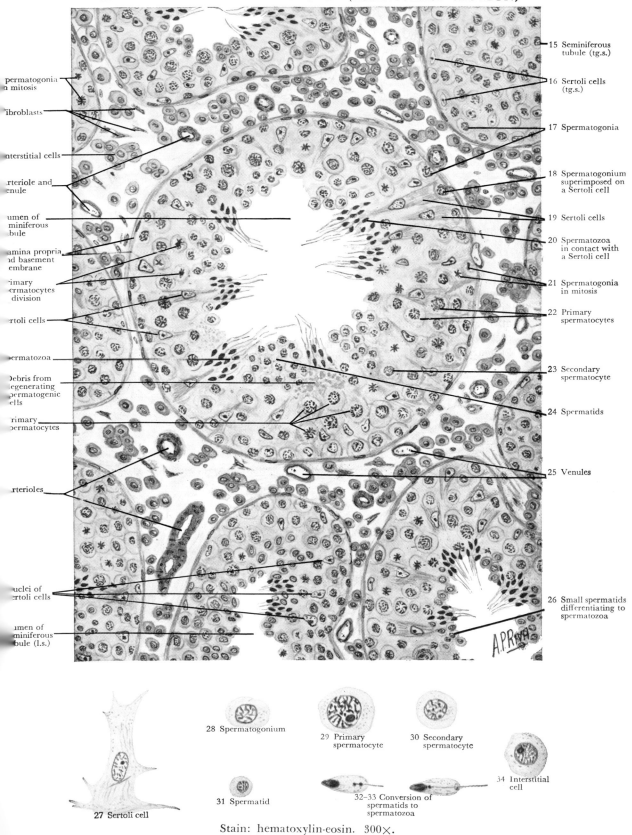

permatogonia
n mitosis

fibroblasts

interstitial cells

rteriole and
enule

umen of
miniferous
bule

amina propria
d basement
embrane

rimary
ermatocytes
division

rtoli cells

ermatozoa

Debris from
egenerating
permatogenic
ells

rimary
permatocytes

rterioles

uclei of
ertoli cells

men of
miniferous
bule (l.s.)

15 Seminiferous
tubule (tg.s.)

16 Sertoli cells
(tg.s.)

17 Spermatogonia

18 Spermatogonium
superimposed on
a Sertoli cell

19 Sertoli cells

20 Spermatozoa
in contact with
a Sertoli cell

21 Spermatogonia
in mitosis

22 Primary
spermatocytes

23 Secondary
spermatocyte

24 Spermatids

25 Venules

26 Small spermatids
differentiating to
spermatozoa

27 Sertoli cell

28 Spermatogonium

29 Primary
spermatocyte

30 Secondary
spermatocyte

31 Spermatid

32-33 Conversion of
spermatids to
spermatozoa

34 Interstitial
cell

Stain: hematoxylin-eosin. 300×.

PLATE 92

DUCTUS DEFERENS (TRANSVERSE SECTION)

The ductus deferens (vas deferens) has a narrow, irregular lumen. The epithelium of the mucosa (7) has a flexuous contour, due to longitudinal crests of the lamina propria (5), which in a transverse section have the appearance of papillae (6). The epithelium is low pseudostratified columnar (7), usually with stereocilia, but these may be absent in places. In the dilated ampulla of the ductus deferens, the epithelium may be similar but without cilia on the surface of the mucosal folds; it becomes columnar secretory in the deep, narrow recesses between the folds.

The mucosa is surrounded by a thick muscular coat disposed in three layers: the inner (3) and outer (1) layers are made up of longitudinal fibers, and the middle layer (2) by circular fibers. Between the muscle fibers there is connective tissue, continuous with that forming the adventitia (4).

PLATE 92

DUCTUS DEFERENS (TRANSVERSE SECTION)

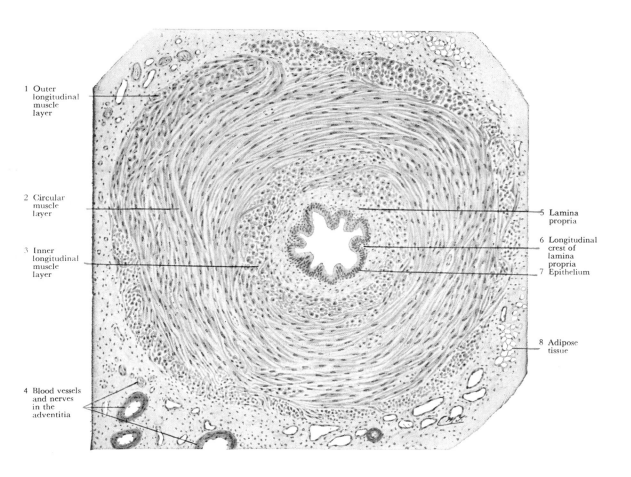

1 Outer longitudinal muscle layer

2 Circular muscle layer

3 Inner longitudinal muscle layer

4 Blood vessels and nerves in the adventitia

5 Lamina propria

6 Longitudinal crest of lamina propria

7 Epithelium

8 Adipose tissue

Stain: hematoxylin-eosin. 40×.

PLATE 93 (Fig. 1)

SEMINAL VESICLE

The mucosa (5) shows primary and secondary folds frequently joined by anastomoses, forming many crypts and cavities (1). A simple columnar epithelium lines the surface, and there are a few rounded basal cells. The muscular coat (2) is made up of fibers placed in several directions; circular fibers predominate in the inner layers, and longitudinal fibers in the outer layers.

The muscular coat is surrounded by loose connective tissue (3) which holds a few small blood vessels.

PLATE 93 (Fig. 2)

PROSTATE

The glandular alveoli (2) seen in a section of prostate are the terminal tubules of many small, irregularly branching tubulo-alveolar glands with wide lumens, thus they present a variety of forms. The epithelium (4) is secretory, generally columnar or pseudostratified, stained lightly in its superficial portion. There is considerable variation, however; it may be squamous or cuboidal. The alveoli contain bodies formed by concentric layers of a calcified organic substance (1).

At first, ducts may be quite similar to alveoli (3), but the epithelium becomes columnar and stains more darkly (5), and finally becomes transitional as the ducts empty into the urethra.

The stroma of fibroelastic connective tissue, with excessive elastic fibers, contains an abundance of smooth muscle fibers (6).

PLATE 93 (Fig. 1)
SEMINAL VESICLE

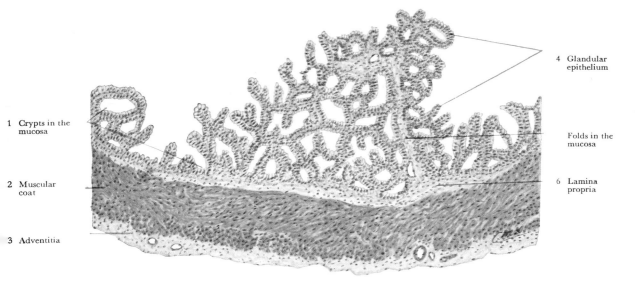

1 Crypts in the mucosa

2 Muscular coat

3 Adventitia

4 Glandular epithelium

Folds in the mucosa

6 Lamina propria

Stain: hematoxylin-eosin. 60×

PLATE 93 (Fig. 2)
PROSTATE

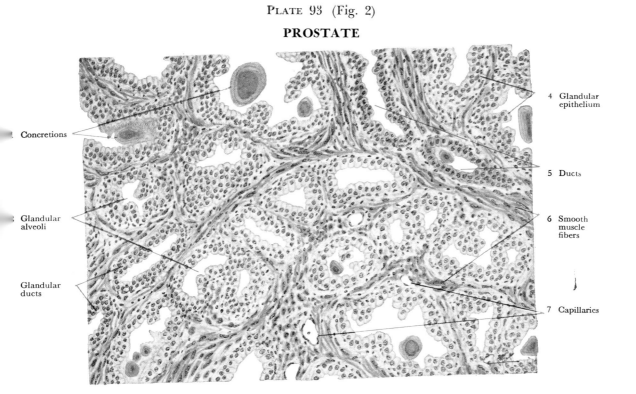

Concretions

Glandular alveoli

Glandular ducts

4 Glandular epithelium

5 Ducts

6 Smooth muscle fibers

7 Capillaries

Stain: hematoxylin-eosin. 180×.

PLATE 94

PENIS (TRANSVERSE SECTION)

A cross-section of the penis reveals sections through the three corpora cavernosa: two dorso-lateral corpora cavernosa penis (9) and a single mid-ventral corpus cavernosum urethrae (corpus spongiosum) (14), which surrounds the urethra (13). A tunic of collagenous fibers lies at the periphery of each of the three corpora. Surrounding the two larger corpora is the tunica albuginea penis (5), which extends between them as the medial septum (10). This septum is better developed at the base of the penis than at the tip; it is frequently pierced by the vascular sinuses of the erectile tissue. Surrounding the corpus spongiosum is the tunica albuginea spongiosum (6).

All three of the cavernosa bodies are bound together by loose connective tissue, the deep penile fascia (Buck's fascia) (4). This fascia in turn is surrounded by the connective tissue of the dermis (2) underlying the epidermis (1). Wisps of smooth muscle fibers, the tunica dartos (3), and an abundance of peripheral blood vessels are to be found embedded in the dermis. Sebaceous glands (7) are embedded in the dermis on the ventral side of the penis.

The core of each corpus cavernosum is occupied by numerous trabeculae, consisting of white fibrous tissue, elastic fibers and smooth muscle fibers. Nerves and blood vessels also lie in the trabeculae. The sinuses of the corpora cavernosa penis receive blood from two sources, the dorsal arterial system and the central (deep) arteries (11). Arterial branches of the latter open directly into sinuses. The corpus cavernosum urethrae receives its blood supply largely from the bulbo-urethral artery. From the sinuses blood exits mainly by way of the superficial veins (12) in the vascularized dermis and the deep dorsal vein (8). Neither the superficial dorsal vein nor the paired dorsal arteries are indicated in this figure.

The urethra in the shaft of the penis is designated as the urethra pars cavernosa or spongiosa (13). Toward the base of the shaft of the penis the urethra is lined with stratified or pseudo-stratified columnar epithelium, but as the epithelium nears the external orifice, it grades into stratified columnar and then stratified squamous epithelium.

Not apparent at this magnification are numerous small but deep invaginations of the mucous membrane, the lacunae of Morgagni, which may contain single or groups of mucous cells. Branched tubular urethral glands of Littré open into these.

PLATE 94

PENIS (TRANSVERSE SECTION)

1 Epidermis

2 Dermis

3 Tunica dartos

4 Deep penile
fascia

5 Tunica
albuginea
penis

6 Tunic
albuginea
spongiosum

7 Sebaceous
gland

8 Deep dorsal
vein

9 Corpus
cavernosum
penis

10 Medial septum

11 Central (deep)
artery

12 Superficial
vein

13 Urethra

14 Corpus
cavernosum
urethrae or
corpus
spongiosum

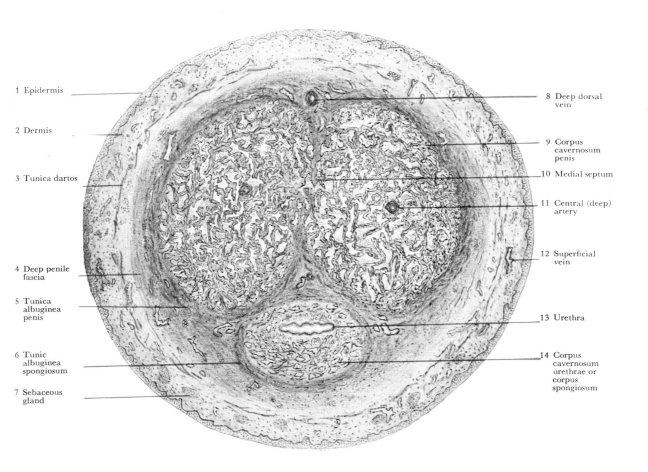

Stain: Hematoxylin-eosin. 12×.

PLATE 95

OVARY (PANORAMIC VIEW)

Numerous follicles in various stages of development are seen embedded in the stroma of the ovary (3, 4, 7, 9, 16, 21, 24). The most numerous are the primary follicles (3, 24) in the cortex; they are the smallest and simplest in structure. The largest of the follicles (16), which has a large cavity full of acidophilic fluid, is a matured Graafian follicle. Those of intermediate sizes are growing follicles. The smaller ones have no follicular cavity (4, 18); the larger ones (7, 9) have cavities of varying sizes. The latter are placed in the deep part of the cortex, separated from the surrounding stroma (8) by enveloping membranes called the follicular thecae (6). All growing vesicular follicles are known as Graafian follicles. In nearly all the follicles, a female sex cell in course of development (23) can be seen. The sex cell is small in the primary follicles, and large in the Graafian follicles. Some follicles never reach maturity, undergo degeneration (involution), and as such are called atretic follicles (11, 17, 22, 25).

In young women the surface of the ovary is covered by simple cuboidal epithelium (1); this becomes flattened in later life. Beneath the epithelium is the tunica albuginea (2).

The stroma of the medulla (20) is made up of connective tissue which is continuous with that of the mesovarium (13). The mesovarium is covered in part by ovarian epithelium, and in part by the peritoneal meso-thelium (14). Blood vessels (10) are particularly abundant in the core of the ovary (20).

The stroma of the cortex (8) is a more primitive type of connective tissue, in which large, spindle-shaped fibroblasts predominate. Coursing in all directions between them are compactly arranged fine collagenous and reticular fibers.

PLATE 95

OVARY (PANORAMIC VIEW)

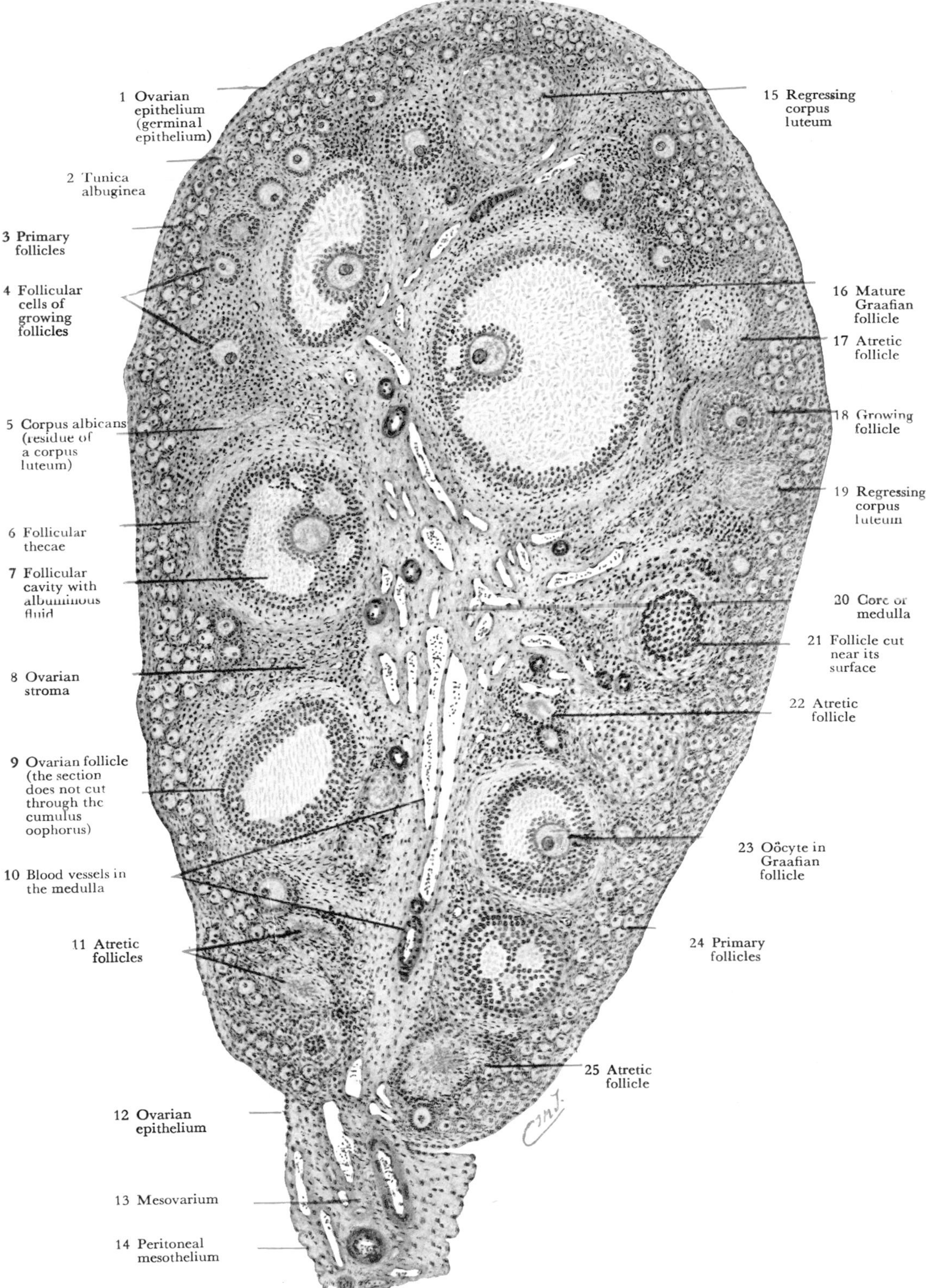

1 Ovarian epithelium (germinal epithelium)

2 Tunica albuginea

3 Primary follicles

4 Follicular cells of growing follicles

5 Corpus albicans (residue of a corpus luteum)

6 Follicular thecae

7 Follicular cavity with albuminous fluid

8 Ovarian stroma

9 Ovarian follicle (the section does not cut through the cumulus oophorus)

10 Blood vessels in the medulla

11 Atretic follicles

12 Ovarian epithelium

13 Mesovarium

14 Peritoneal mesothelium

15 Regressing corpus luteum

16 Mature Graafian follicle

17 Atretic follicle

18 Growing follicle

19 Regressing corpus luteum

20 Core or medulla

21 Follicle cut near its surface

22 Atretic follicle

23 Oöcyte in Graafian follicle

24 Primary follicles

25 Atretic follicle

Stain: hematoxylin-eosin. 60×.

PLATE 96 (Fig. 1)

OVARY: CORTEX, PRIMARY AND MATURING FOLLICLES

Numerous primary follicles lie in the outer layer of the ovarian stroma, immediately beneath the tunica albuginea (2). Each follicle consists of a female sex cell (5) surrounded by a single layer of flattened follicular cells (6).

Intermediate follicles in later stages of development are seen at (7) and (4). In the former, the developing sex cell is surrounded with a single layer of follicular cells, which have become cuboidal. In the latter, the follicular cells have multiplied by mitosis (3) and form a stratified epithelium of columnar cells around the developing sex cell. Several layers surrounding the sex cell are clearly in evidence: the zona pellucida (12), a non-cellular layer immediately adjacent to the sex cell; the follicular cells (10) which will become the membrana granulosa; and a layer of stroma cells, which will become the thecae (9), externa and interna, of more mature follicles. Within the female sex cell is a large eccentrically placed nucleus (germinal vesicle) (11) with a conspicuous nucleolus (germinal spot).

An atretic follicle (14), containing the remnants of a disintegrated sex cell, is shown in the lower right-hand corner.

The ovarian epithelium (1) is composed of cuboidal cells. Beneath it lies the tunica albuginea (2), composed of dense connective tissue.

PLATE 96 (Fig. 2)

OVARY: WALL OF A MATURE GRAAFIAN FOLLICLE

The human female sex cell (11) at this stage of development is a primary oöcyte. Surrounding it is the zona pellucida (10). Follicular fluid (8), secreted by the follicular cells, fills the mature follicle (see Plate 95, 16). The maturing sex cell, surrounded by follicular cells, projects into the follicular fluid, forming a hillock called the cumulus oöphorus (12). The follicular cells nearest the ovum become columnar and form a radially arranged layer around the ovum, the corona radiata (9). Additional follicular cells (6) surround the central cavity. Collectively, because of their granular appearance in sections through a mature follicle, they are called the membrana granulosa. Follicular fluid fills the central cavity. Isolated smaller intercellular accumulations of follicular fluid may occur (14), and if these are rounded and stain deeply, they are designated as Call-Exner vacuoles (3, 7).

Two thecae are peripheral to the follicular cells: the theca interna (5) and the theca externa (2). Peripheral to them lies the stroma of the cortex (1).

PLATE 96

OVARY

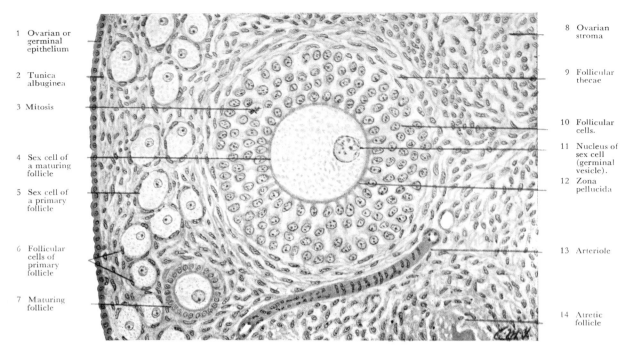

1 Ovarian or germinal epithelium

2 Tunica albuginea

3 Mitosis

4 Sex cell of a maturing follicle

5 Sex cell of a primary follicle

6 Follicular cells of primary follicle

7 Maturing follicle

8 Ovarian stroma

9 Follicular thecae

10 Follicular cells.

11 Nucleus of sex cell (germinal vesicle).

12 Zona pellucida

13 Arteriole

14 Atretic follicle

FIG. 1. — *Cortex, primary and maturing follicles.*
Stain: hematoxylin-eosin. 320×.

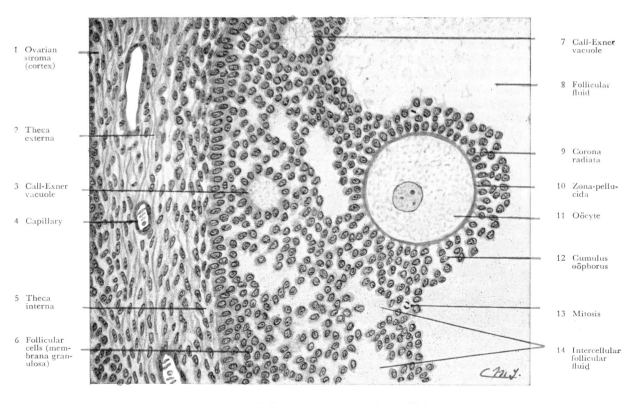

1 Ovarian stroma (cortex)

2 Theca externa

3 Call-Exner vacuole

4 Capillary

5 Theca interna

6 Follicular cells (membrana granulosa)

7 Call-Exner vacuole

8 Follicular fluid

9 Corona radiata

10 Zona-pellucida

11 Oöcyte

12 Cumulus oöphorus

13 Mitosis

14 Intercellular follicular fluid

FIG. 2. — *Wall of a mature Graafian follicle.*
Stain: hematoxylin-eosin. 320×.

PLATE 97 (Fig. 1)

CORPUS LUTEUM (PANORAMIC VIEW)

In cross section a corpus luteum appears as a highly folded band of glandular tissue, made up of anastomosing columns or trabeculae of secretory cells (3). A fibrous capsule (1) surrounds the glandular tissue and separates it from the ovarian stroma (4). The core is formed of loose connective tissue (7), surrounding a small blood clot (8), partly invaded by connective tissue.

Trabeculae of connective tissue (2, 6) from the fibrous capsule (1) penetrate the glandular tissue, but do not reach the deeper parts of the glandular epithelium. Numerous blood vessels (5) lie in the surrounding connective tissue of the ovarian stroma.

PLATE 97 (Fig. 2)

CORPUS LUTEUM (PERIPHERAL MARGIN)

The granulosa-lutein cells (7) make up the mass of the corpus luteum. Between the anastomosing columns of cells are numerous capillaries (8), which, together with accompanying fine connective tissue, have proliferated from the theca interna, now the theca-lutein layer (2). Granulosa-lutein cells (7) are large, lightly-stained in part (in this specimen) because of lipid inclusions, and have large, vesicular nuclei. Theca-lutein cells are limited to the periphery of the corpus luteum and to the depressions between folds (2); the cells (2) are smaller than granulosa-lutein cells, the granular cytoplasm stains more deeply, nuclei are smaller and darker.

Numerous blood vessels are seen in the surrounding stroma (1, 3, 4). The thin fibrous capsule (5) represents a concentration of stroma (not well demonstrated here).

PLATE 97

CORPUS LUTEUM

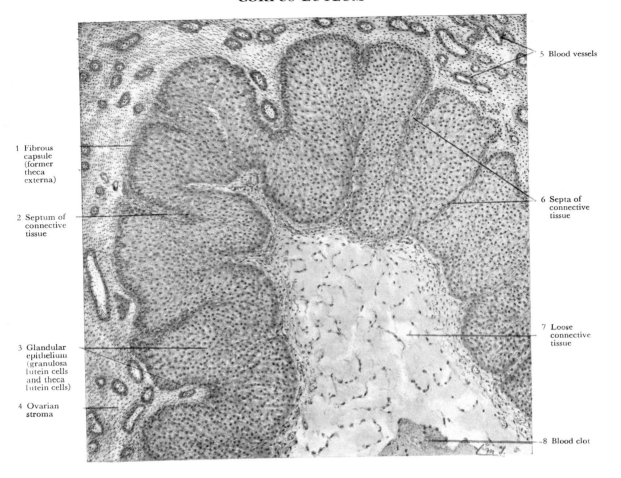

1 Fibrous capsule (former theca externa)

2 Septum of connective tissue

3 Glandular epithelium (granulosa lutein cells and theca lutein cells)

4 Ovarian stroma

5 Blood vessels

6 Septa of connective tissue

7 Loose connective tissue

8 Blood clot

FIG. 1. — *Panoramic view.*
Stain: hematoxylin-eosin. 80×.

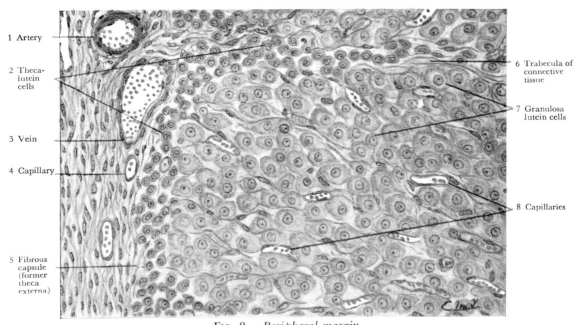

1 Artery

2 Theca-lutein cells

3 Vein

4 Capillary

5 Fibrous capsule (former theca externa)

6 Trabecula of connective tissue

7 Granulosa lutein cells

8 Capillaries

FIG. 2. — *Peripheral margin.*
Stain: hematoxylin-eosin. 250×.

PLATE 98 (Fig. 1)

UTERINE TUBE: AMPULLA (PANORAMIC VIEW, TRANSVERSE SECTION)

The stellate lumen of the uterine tube (Fallopian tube or oviduct) is lined by a mucosa with large ramified folds (9). The surface epithelium is of the simple columnar type (10). The muscular coat is made up of fibers distributed in many directions, predominantly circular in the inner layers (1) and longitudinal in the outer layers (6). Numerous small blood vessels (3, 4, 5) lie in the interfascicular connective tissue (2). The tube is surrounded by a tunica serosa, covered by mesothelium (7).

PLATE 98 (Fig. 2)

UTERINE TUBE: MUCOSA

The epithelium (1) is composed of ciliated columnar cells (3) and peg-shaped non-ciliated secretory cells (4). The cilia beat toward the uterus. The proportion of these two cell types varies with stages of the menstrual cycle.

The lamina propria is a loose connective tissue, with thin fibers and numerous fibroblasts, many of which have processes and are apparently less differentiated than ordinary fibroblasts. This connective tissue is capable of reacting like the stroma of the uterus if an incipient embryo becomes inadvertently planted in the wall of the tube; many of the fibroblasts become decidual cells.

PLATE 98

UTERINE TUBE: AMPULLA

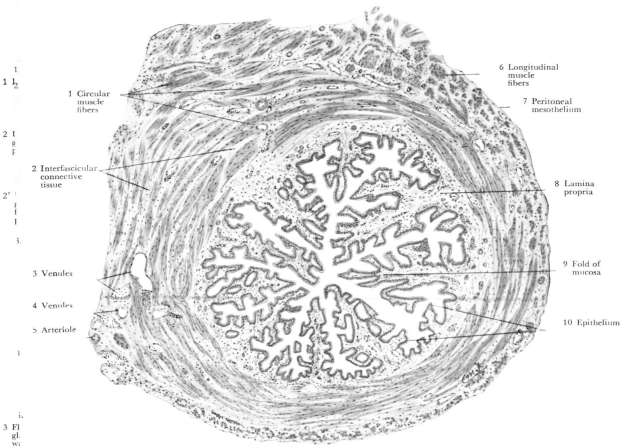

1 Circular muscle fibers

2 Interfascicular connective tissue

3 Venules

4 Venules

5 Arteriole

6 Longitudinal muscle fibers

7 Peritoneal mesothelium

8 Lamina propria

9 Fold of mucosa

10 Epithelium

FIG. 1. — *Panoramic view.*
Stain: hematoxylin-eosin. 40×.

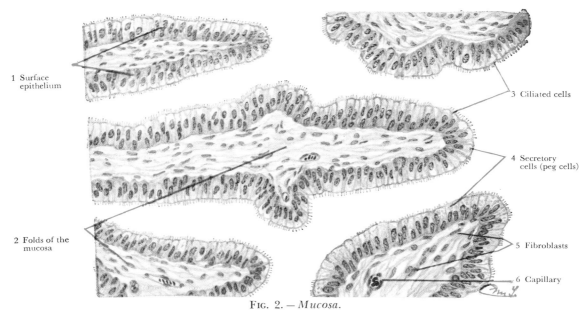

1 Surface epithelium

2 Folds of the mucosa

3 Ciliated cells

4 Secretory cells (peg cells)

5 Fibroblasts

6 Capillary

FIG. 2. — *Mucosa.*
Stain: hematoxylin-eosin. 320×.

PLATE 102

Fig. 1. PLACENTA: FIVE MONTHS' PREGNANCY

The upper part of the plate corresponds to the fetal portion of the placenta (10, 11). The maternal placenta includes the outer portion of the endometrium (12–14) which lies beneath the fetal placenta. Below this is the basal portion of the endometrium, containing the deep parts of the uterine glands (15), which is not sloughed off during parturition. A small area of myometrium (17) is seen in the lower field.

On the upper surface of the section is seen the squamous epithelium of the amnion (1). The layer of connective tissue (2) represents merged connective tissue of the amnion and chorion. Below this is the chorionic plate (3, 10). Details of the trophoblast are not distinguishable at this magnification.

Anchoring villi arising from the chorionic plate (4, upper leaders) extend to the uterine wall and embed in the decidua basalis (7). This continuity is not seen in this plate, but larger units in the fetal placenta probably represent sections of anchoring villi (4, lower leader). These will increase in size and complexity.

Innumerable floating villi are seen (chorion frondosum), sectioned in various planes (5, 11) because of their outgrowth in all directions from the anchoring villi. They "float" in the intervillous spaces (6) which are filled with maternal blood. The structure of these villi is shown in Fig. 2.

The maternal portion of the placenta, or decidua basalis, shows anchoring villi embedded in it (7), groups of large decidual cells (8) as well as typical stroma, distal portions of uterine glands which are in various stages of regression (14) and which usually disappear entirely later, and maternal blood vessels, recognized by their size or by red blood corpuscles in their lumens (9). A maternal blood vessel is seen opening into an intervillous space (13).

Coiled arteries (16) and basal portions of uterine glands (15) are present in the deep zone of the endometrium. Fibrin deposits are seen on the surface of the decidua basalis (12). These will increase in volume and extent.

Fig. 2. CHORIONIC VILLI (PLACENTA AT FIVE MONTHS)

The plate shows several chorionic villi, from the above placenta of a fetus of five months, at a higher magnification. It is seen that the trophoblastic epithelium is composed of an external layer of syncitial cells, the syncitial trophoblast (1) and another deeper layer of well outlined cells, the cytotrophoblast or layer of Langhans (2). In the interior of the villus, which is embryonic connective tissue (3), one finds fetal blood vessels (5) which are branches of umbilical arteries and veins; both nucleated and non-nucleated erythrocytes may be present. Intervillous spaces (4) contain maternal blood, erythrocytes are non-nucleated. One of the villi shown is attached to the endometrium (6). Several decidual cells (7) are seen in the stroma.

Fig. 3. CHORIONIC VILLI (PLACENTA AT TERM)

This plate shows several chorionic villi from a placenta of a fetus at term. In contrast to the villi in Fig. 2, the chorionic epithelium here is present only as syncitial trophoblast (1), whose syncitial character is more pronounced than in Fig. 2. The connective tissue (2) is more differentiated, showing more fibers, fewer typical fibroblasts, and many large, rounded Hofbauer cells or macrophages (4). Fetal blood vessels are numerous (3), having increased in complexity of branching as pregnancy progressed.

PLATE 102. PLACENTA

FIG. 1. PLACENTA: FIVE MONTHS' PREGNANCY
(PANORAMIC VIEW)

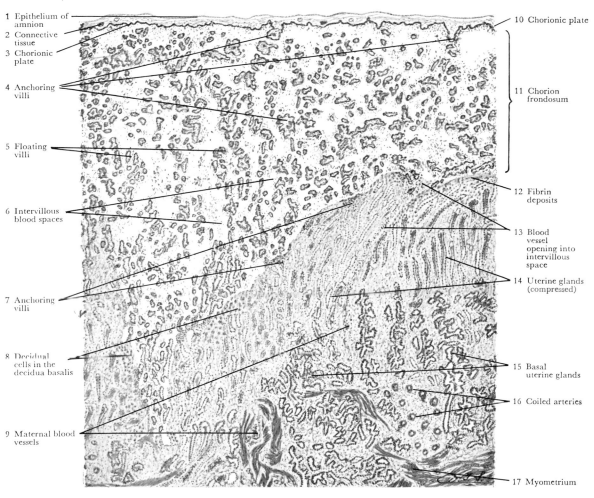

1 Epithelium of amnion
2 Connective tissue
3 Chorionic plate
4 Anchoring villi
5 Floating villi
6 Intervillous blood spaces
7 Anchoring villi
8 Decidual cells in the decidua basalis
9 Maternal blood vessels

10 Chorionic plate
11 Chorion frondosum
12 Fibrin deposits
13 Blood vessel opening into intervillous space
14 Uterine glands (compressed)
15 Basal uterine glands
16 Coiled arteries
17 Myometrium

Stain: hematoxylin-eosin. 10×.

FIG. 2. CHORIONIC VILLI
(Placenta at Five Months)

1 Syncitial trophoblast
2 Cytotrophoblast
3 Embryonic connective tissue
4 Intervillous space
5 Fetal blood vessels
6 Attached villus
7 Decidual cell

Stain: hematoxylin eosin. 350×.

FIG. 3. CHORIONIC VILLI
(Placenta at Term)

1 Syncitial trophoblast
2 Connective tissue
3 Fetal blood vessels
4 Hofbauer cells (macrophages)

Stain: hematoxylin-eosin. 350×.

— 217 —

PLATE 103

CERVIX (LONGITUDINAL SECTION)

The epithelium lining the right side of the section and the lower end is of the stratified squamous type (7); it covers the outer or peripheral surface of the cervix. The epithelium lining the left side of the section, corresponding to the inner surface, or endocervix, is of the simple columnar type (1). Numerous mucous glands with an irregular lumen (2), situated in the underlying lamina propria, open into the endocervix. The lamina propria of the endocervix is still a "cellular" type of connective tissue but less so than in the uterus; fibroblasts are numerous, the fibers are mainly collagenous. Under the stratified squamous epithelium, the connective tissue becomes a moderately dense irregular type (8).

The central part of the section shows bundles of smooth muscle fibers which have been cut transversally (3, 9). There are also blood vessels of medium size (4); those in the superficial layers are smaller (10).

At the fornix (6), the epithelium covering the outer surface of the cervix is continuous with the epithelium lining the vagina.

In the lower left corner of the illustration (5), the epithelium of the outer surface suddenly changes to that of the inner surface of the cervix; this corresponds to the os or vaginal opening of the cervical canal.

PLATE 103

CERVIX (LONGITUDINAL SECTION)

1 Epithelium of the endocervix

6 Fornix

2 Cervical glands

7 Vaginal epithelium

3 Smooth muscle fibers

8 Lamina propria

4 Veins

9 Smooth muscle fibers

10 Venules

5 Os, or vaginal opening of the cervical canal

11 Lymphatic nodule

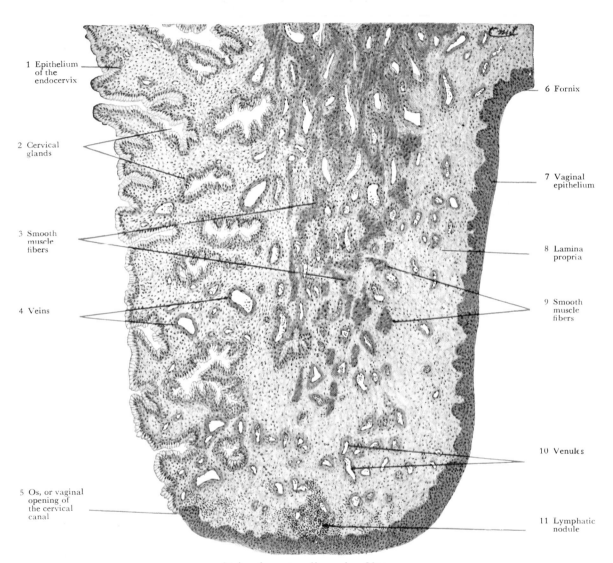

Stain: hematoxylin-eosin. 20×.

PLATE 104 (Fig. 1)

VAGINA (LONGITUDINAL SECTION)

The mucosa has numerous folds (5) and a papillary lamina propria (2), and is well supplied with small blood vessels (4). The surface epithelium is of the stratified squamous type (1); desquamation of the superficial cells often occurs. Normally, the superficial cells are not keratinized.

The muscular coat is made up predominantly of longitudinal (6) and oblique (8) fibers; circular fibers (10) are less numerous and more frequently found in the inner layers.

The adventitia (7) is shown only in part; in it are numerous veins (9), which form a vascular plexus.

Nodules of lymphatic tissue (3) are scattered throughout the lamina propria.

PLATE 104 (Fig. 2)

GLYCOGEN IN HUMAN VAGINAL EPITHELIUM

Glycogen is a prominent component of the cells in the vaginal epithelium, except in the deepest layers, where normally there is little or none. It accumulates during the follicular phase, reaching its maximum just before ovulation. It can be demonstrated by the use of iodine vapor, or iodine solution in mineral oil (Mancini's method). Glycogen stains a reddish-purple.

Figures (a) and (b) were similarly prepared by fixation in absolute alcohol and formaldehyde. In (a), one sees the amount of glycogen present during the interfollicular phase of the cycle. In (b), during the follicular phase, the amount of glycogen is increased, especially in the intermediate layers, but extending also into the more superficial cells.

Figure (c), from the same specimen as (b), but fixed by the Altmann-Gersch method (freezing and drying in a vacuum) with less shrinkage of tissue, shows that glycogen is abundant during the follicular phase, and that it is distributed diffusely throughout the cytoplasm.

PLATE 104

Fig. 1. VAGINA (LONGITUDINAL SECTION)

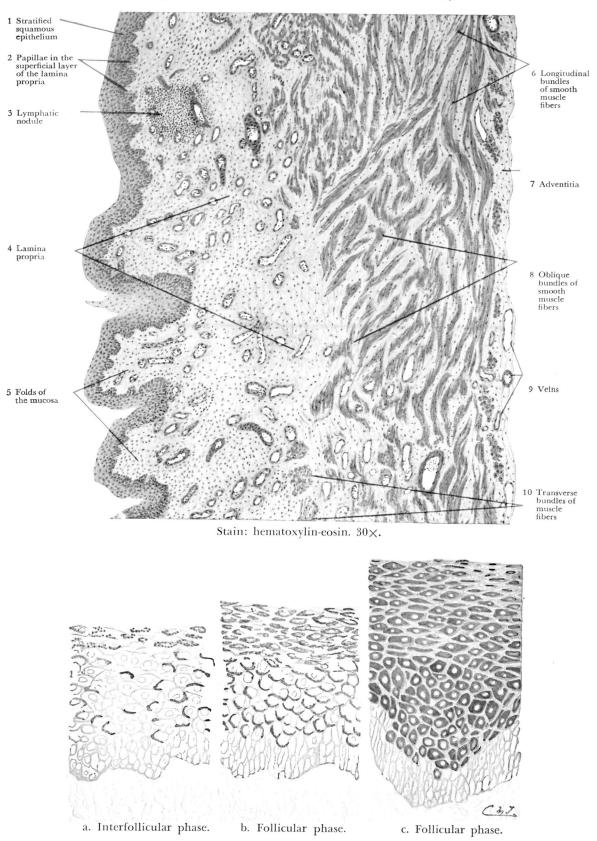

1 Stratified squamous epithelium

2 Papillae in the superficial layer of the lamina propria

3 Lymphatic nodule

4 Lamina propria

5 Folds of the mucosa

6 Longitudinal bundles of smooth muscle fibers

7 Adventitia

8 Oblique bundles of smooth muscle fibers

9 Veins

10 Transverse bundles of muscle fibers

Stain: hematoxylin-eosin. 30×.

a. Interfollicular phase.   b. Follicular phase.   c. Follicular phase.

Fig. 2. GLYCOGEN IN HUMAN VAGINAL EPITHELIUM

Stain: Mancini's iodine technique.

PLATE 105

VAGINA: EXFOLIATE CYTOLOGY

This plate shows smears, from vaginal material obtained by suction, on different days of the menstrual cycle of a normal woman, and also smears obtained during the early months of pregnancy and during menopause. The Shorr trichrome stain employed (Biebrich scarlet, Orange G and Fast Green) plus Harris hematoxylin, facilitates recognition of the different cellular types.

Fig. 7 presents individual cell types. At (a) is a superficial acidophil of the vaginal mucosa. It is flat, somewhat irregular in outline, is from 35 to 65 μ in diameter, has a small pyknotic nucleus, and ample cytoplasm tinted an orange color. At (b) is a similar superficial basophil with bluish-green cytoplasm. At (c) is an intermediate cell from the intermediate stratum of the vaginal epithelium. It is flattened like the superficial cells, but smaller (20 to 40 μ), and has a basophilic blue green-cytoplasm. Its nucleus is somewhat larger and often vesicular. Cells at (d) are intermediate cells in profile (navicular cells), characterized by their elongated form with folded borders and an elongated nucleus placed eccentrically. At (e) are represented cells of the deep layers of the vaginal epithelium, the basal cells. The larger ones, considered to be the more superficial cells, are called parabasal cells. All are rounded or oval, from 12 to 15 μ in diameter, and have a relatively large nucleus with a more prominent chromatin network. Most of them are basophilic.

Fig. 1 represents a vaginal smear from the 5th day of the menstrual cycle (post menstrual phase). In predominance are intermediate cells (1) from the outer layers of the intermediate stratum (transitions to the deeper superficial cells). A few superficial acidophils and basophils (2) and a few leucocytes are also present.

Fig. 2, a smear from the 14th day of the cycle (ovulatory stage), is characterized by predominance of large superficial acidophils (8), the scarcity of superficial basophils (10) and intermediate cells (9), and the absence of leucocytes. It is the expression of the high estrogenic level achieved by the time of ovulation, and is therefore called the "follicular type" smear. The superficial cells "mature" with increase in estrogen and become acidophilic. This same type of smear can be obtained from a menopausic patient when she is under intensive estrogenic treatment.

Fig. 3, from the 21st day of the cycle, represents the luteal stage (progestational stage), under the influence of high levels of progesterone and diminished estrogens. In predominance are large intermediate cells (precornified superficial cells) with folded borders (3) which aggregate into groups. Superficial acidophils (4), superficial basophils (5) and leucocytes are scarce.

Fig. 4 represents the premenstrual stage on the 28th day of the cycle, characterized by the great predominance of intermediate cells with folded borders (13, 14) which tend to form groups (14), by an increase in leucocytes (12), a scarcity of superficial cells (11), and by an abundance of mucus which gives a blurred aspect to these preparations.

Fig. 5, from a 3 months' pregnancy, shows predominantly intermediate cells of the navicular type, many with folded borders (6). Typically, these form dense groups or conglomerations (7). Superficial cells and leucocytes are very scarce.

Fig. 6. The smear during menopause is quite different from all others. In a typical "atrophic" smear, the dominant cells are the rounded or oval basal cells of varied diameters (17). Intermediate cells are scarce (15), leucocytes are abundant (16). However, menopausal smears will vary, depending on the stage of menopause and the estrogen levels present.

Vaginal exfoliate cytology is correlated with the ovarian cycle. Its study permits recognition of the degree of follicular activity, whether normally or after estrogenic or other therapy, and provides information (together with cells from the endocervix) for the recognition of regional malignant processes.

PLATE 105

VAGINA: EXFOLIATE CYTOLOGY (VAGINAL SMEARS)

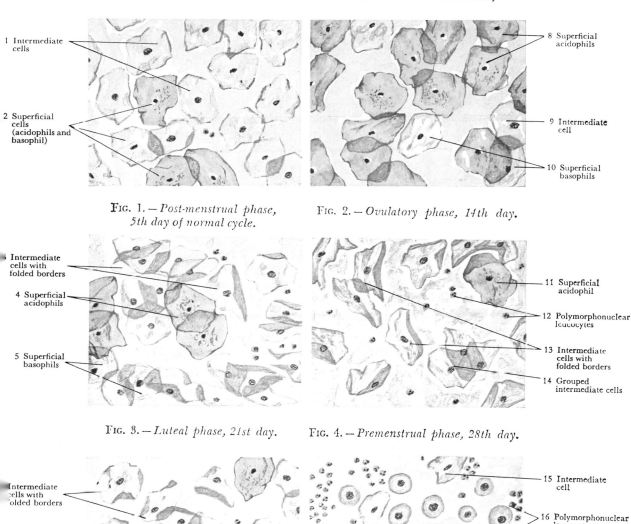

1 Intermediate cells

2 Superficial cells (acidophils and basophil)

8 Superficial acidophils

9 Intermediate cell

10 Superficial basophils

FIG. 1. — *Post-menstrual phase, 5th day of normal cycle.*

FIG. 2. — *Ovulatory phase, 14th day.*

Intermediate cells with folded borders

4 Superficial acidophils

5 Superficial basophils

11 Superficial acidophil

12 Polymorphonuclear leucocytes

13 Intermediate cells with folded borders

14 Grouped intermediate cells

FIG. 3. — *Luteal phase, 21st day.*

FIG. 4. — *Premenstrual phase, 28th day.*

Intermediate cells with folded borders

glomerate of icular cells

15 Intermediate cell

16 Polymorphonuclear leucocytes

17 Basal cells

FIG. 5. — *Three months' pregnancy.*

FIG. 6. — *Menopause, atrophic phase.*

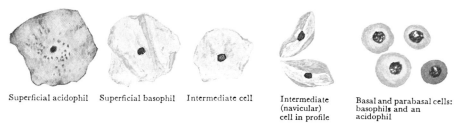

Superficial acidophil   Superficial basophil   Intermediate cell

Intermediate (navicular) cell in profile

Basal and parabasal cells: basophils and an acidophil

FIG. 7. — *Types of cells found in vaginal smears of a normal cycle.*

Stain: Shorr's trichrome. 250 × and 450 ×.

PLATE 106 (Fig. 1)

MAMMARY GLAND, INACTIVE

The central area of the illustration shows one lobule. Ducts (5) and secretory tubules (3, 9) are of similar structure and difficult to distinguish one from the other. Both are surrounded by intralobular loose connective tissue (4), with fine collagenous fibers and numerous fibroblasts. Dense interlobular connective tissue (2), with many blood vessels (6, 8) and groups of adipose cells (10), separates the glandular lobes.

PLATE 106 (Fig. 2)

MAMMARY GLAND DURING THE FIRST HALF OF PREGNANCY

Proliferation of the secretory tubules (6) occurs in each glandular lobule (1) during pregnancy. The relative quantity of intralobular connective tissue (7) thus appears less than in the active gland. Some of the glandular alveoli are filled with secretion (5). Other alveoli (2) lack a lumen, being in process of development. There are intralobular (9) and interlobular (4) ducts; the latter are usually larger than the former. The largest ducts are lactiferous ducts (8), which collect the secretion of a lobule and open at the apex of the nipple.

The loose intralobular connective tissue (7) provides space for the expanding alveoli and intralobular ducts. In addition to numerous fibroblasts, other cells are present during pregnancy and lactation, particularly lymphocytes and plasma cells.

PLATE 106

MAMMARY GLAND

1 Part of a lobule

2 Interlobular connective tissue

3 Secretory tubules

4 Intralobular loose connective tissue

5 Duct

6 Artery

7 Duct

8 Arterioles

9 Secretory tubules

10 Adipose cells

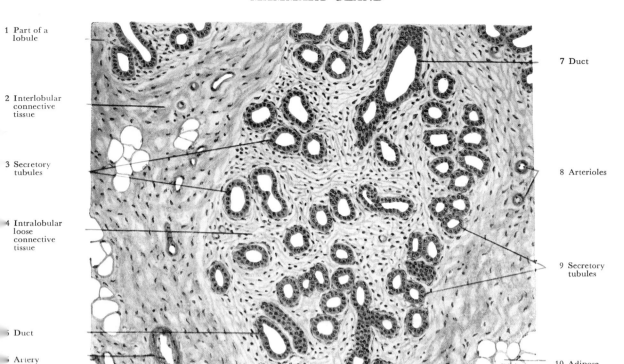

FIG. 1. — *Mammary gland, inactive.*
Stain: hematoxylin-eosin. 90×.

Glandular lobules

Alveoli (tubules)

Interlobular connective tissue

Interlobular duct

Alveoli with albuminous secretion

6 Glandular alveoli

7 Intralobular connective tissue.

8 Lactiferous duct

9 Intralobular ducts

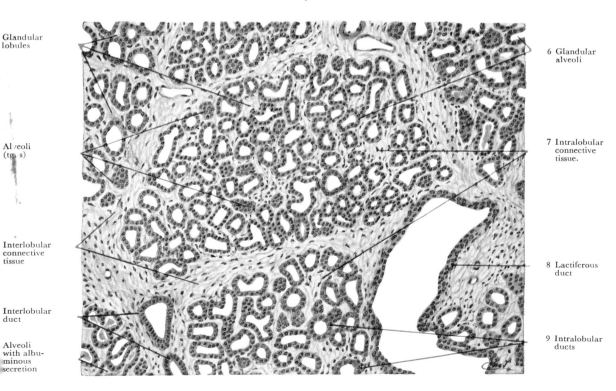

FIG. 2. — *Mammary gland during the first half of pregnancy.*
Stain: hematoxylin-eosin. 90×.

PLATE 107

EYELID (SAGITTAL SECTION)

The outer surface of the eyelid is shown at the left; the inner surface, adjacent to the eyeball, to the right. The epithelium of the anterior or outer aspect of the eyelid is covered by stratified squamous epithelium (1). The posterior or inner aspect of the eyelid is covered by the palpebral conjunctiva (14), of which the epithelium is thinner, of low stratified columnar type, and not cornified. Both epithelia lie on a papillary dermis, which is continuous with the underlying connective tissue (4). The lamina of dense fibrous tissue on each side of the Meibomian glands (12) is termed the tarsus (13).

Three sets of muscle fibers are in evidence: the palpebral part of the striated orbicularis muscle (3), the striated ciliary muscle (muscle of Riolan) (16), and the non-striated muscle fibers forming the tarsal muscle (muscle of Müller) (8).

Each eyelash (17) arises from a well-developed hair follicle, one of which is cut tangentially in the illustration. Rudimentary hair follicles (2) are to be found on the anterior aspect of the eyelid; they form the fine down on the lid.

Numerous glands occur. Specialized sebaceous glands, Meibomian glands (12), lie in the tarsus; their products empty into a common duct (15), which opens behind the hair follicles. Other sebaceous glands, Zeiss' glands (7) are attached to the hair follicles of the eyelashes. Sweat glands, Moll's glands (6), also lie in the vicinity of the hair follicles of the eyelashes. The accessory lacrimal gland (Krause's gland) (10) lies at the fornix, or junction of the palpebral conjunctiva with the ocular conjunctiva (not shown). Other small accessory lacrimal glands, the tarsal lacrimal glands (of Wolfring), lie in the connective tissue above the tarsal plate (in the region of the three blood vessels in this figure), and open by ducts on the surface of the conjunctiva. They are scattered and vary in number, thus are not necessarily present in every section.

An infiltration of lymphocytes is shown, but not labelled, in the vicinity of the accessory lacrimal glands.

PLATE 107

EYELID (SAGITTAL SECTION)

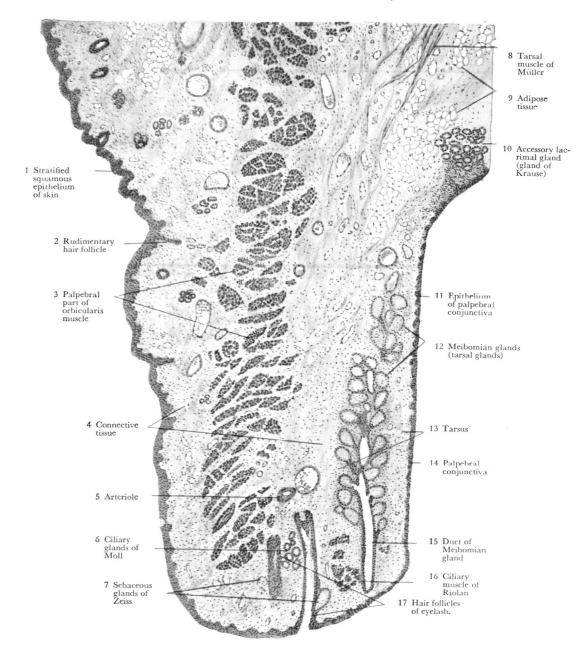

1 Glandular
  alveoli

2 Intralobular
  ducts

Basket cell

Interlobular
connective
tissue

Blood ves

Chromato

Pigment c

Rods

Cones

Outer limi
membrane
Nuclei of c

Nuclei of r

Outer plex
layer

Nuclei of bi
horizontal,
amacrine ar
Muller's cell

Inner plexifo
layer

Ganglion cell
layer

Muller's fiber
Fibers of the
optic nerve
Inner limiting
membrane

1 Cornea

2 Ocular
  conjunctiva

3 Sclera
4 Ciliary
  muscle
5 Suspensory
  ligament

6 Lens

1 Anterior
  epithelium
2 Bowman's
  membrane

3 Substantia
  propria

4 Descemet's
  membrane
5 Posterior
  epithelium

7 Retina
8 Choroid

9 Sclera

10 Central
   blood
   vessels

11 External
   sheath of
   optic nerve
   (dura mater

1 Stratified
  squamous
  epithelium
  of skin

2 Rudimentary
  hair follicle

3 Palpebral
  part of
  orbicularis
  muscle

4 Connective
  tissue

5 Arteriole

6 Ciliary
  glands of
  Moll

7 Sebaceous
  glands of
  Zeiss

8 Tarsal
  muscle of
  Müller

9 Adipose
  tissue

10 Accessory lac-
   rimal gland
   (gland of
   Krause)

11 Epithelium
   of palpebral
   conjunctiva

12 Meibomian glands
   (tarsal glands)

13 Tarsus

14 Palpebral
   conjunctiva

15 Duct of
   Meibomian
   gland

16 Ciliary
   muscle of
   Riolan

17 Hair follicles
   of eyelash.

Stain: hematoxylin-eosin. 20×.

PLATE 111 (Fig. 1)

INNER EAR: COCHLEA (VERTICAL SECTION)

A bony tube (6, 15, 17) is twisted in a spiral around the columella or modiolus (16). The fibers of the cochlear nerve (9) are included inside the modiolus, which also contains groups of nerve cell bodies (13) belonging to the spiral ganglion of Corti.

The lumen of the tube is divided by a bony lamina, the osseous spiral lamina (8), continued by the basilar membrane (7), inserted on the free edge of the lamina and on the spiral ligament (14) which lines the inner aspect of the outer wall of the bony tube. The lower compartment is the scala tympani (4); the upper compartment is the scala vestibuli (2). Reissner's vestibular membrane (5, 10) separates the cochlear duct (3) from the scala vestibuli (2). Communication between the scala tympani and the scala vestibuli is established by a small orifice at the top end of the tube as the helicotrema (1).

The specialized cells for receiving vibrations and transmitting them as nerve impulses to the brain lie on the basilar membrane (7) and are known as the organ of Corti (12). The tectorial membrane (11) overlies the organ of Corti.

PLATE 111 (Fig. 2)

INNER EAR: COCHLEAR DUCT

The cochlear duct (7) is separated from the scala vestibuli (4) by the vestibular membrane (Reissner's membrane) (5). The lateral wall of the cochlear duct is formed by the stria vascularis (13), a vascularized pseudo-epithelium. This epithelium covers an area of fibrous connective tissue, the spiral ligament (14).

The spiral limbus (6) forms the median floor of the cochlear duct; the limbus is composed of fibers of connective tissue covered by columnar epithelium. The lateral extension of this epithelium is the tectorial membrane (9), which overlies part of the organ of Corti.

The organ of Corti (10) is a set of highly specialized sensory cells extending from the spiral limbus to the spiral ligament. At least some of the cells of the organ of Corti, in a way as yet undetermined, are thought to convert sound waves into sound impulses to the brain. The nomenclature of the cellular entities of the organ of Corti is complex and is omitted here as being too detailed for the student of general histology.

The lateral extension of the osseous spiral lamina (1) supports the spiral limbus. The basilar membrane (11) supports the organ of Corti.

The basilar membrane (11) consists of a plate of vascularized fibrous connective tissue underlying a thinner plate of basilar fibers (unlabelled). On these basilar fibers lies the organ of Corti.

From the spiral ganglion of Corti (3), fibers of the cochlear nerve (2) extend to the sensory cells of the organ of Corti.

PLATE 111

INNER EAR

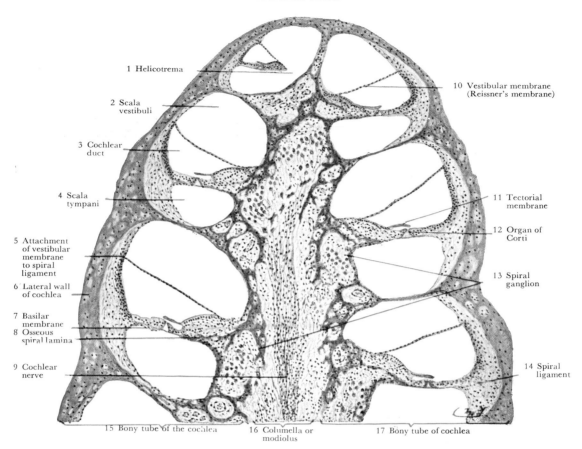

1 Helicotrema
2 Scala vestibuli
3 Cochlear duct
4 Scala tympani
5 Attachment of vestibular membrane to spiral ligament
6 Lateral wall of cochlea
7 Basilar membrane
8 Osseous spiral lamina
9 Cochlear nerve

10 Vestibular membrane (Reissner's membrane)
11 Tectorial membrane
12 Organ of Corti
13 Spiral ganglion
14 Spiral ligament

15 Bony tube of the cochlea
16 Columella or modiolus
17 Bony tube of cochlea

FIG. 1. — *Cochlea (vertical section).*
Stain: hematoxylin-eosin. 55×.

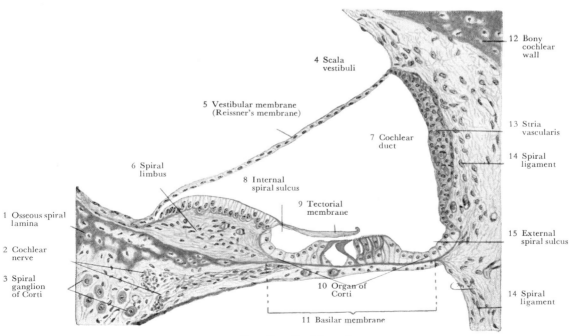

4 Scala vestibuli
5 Vestibular membrane (Reissner's membrane)
6 Spiral limbus
8 Internal spiral sulcus
9 Tectorial membrane
1 Osseous spiral lamina
2 Cochlear nerve
3 Spiral ganglion of Corti
7 Cochlear duct
10 Organ of Corti
11 Basilar membrane

12 Bony cochlear wall
13 Stria vascularis
14 Spiral ligament
15 External spiral sulcus
14 Spiral ligament

FIG. 2. — *Cochlear duct.*
Stain: hematoxylin-eosin. 200×.

INDEX

A

B

Burdach's column (Fasciculus cuneatus), 74, 75

C

CALL-EXNER vacuole, 204, 205
Calyx, 172, 173
Canaliculi of bone, 40, 41
— bile, of liver, 156, 157
— of teeth, 112, 113
Cardia, 128, 129
Cardiac glands, 128, 129
Cartilage, 36-39
— fibrous, 38, 39
— elastic, 38, 39
— hyaline, 36, 37
— tracheal, 166, 167
Cell, amacrine, 232, 233
— argentaffine, 142, 143
— bipolar, 232, 233
— centroacinar, 162, 163
— Paneth, 142, 143
— Sertoli, 194, 195
Cementum of bone, 40, 41
— of teeth, 112, 113
Centroacinar cell, 162, 163
Cerebellum, 78, 79
— cortical layers of, 78, 79
Cerebral cortex, layers of, 80, 81
Cervical glands, 218, 219
Cervix, 218, 219
Chief cells (Principal cells) of the parathyroids, 188, 189
— — of stomach, 130-135
Chondrinballen, 36, 37
Chondroblast, 37
Chondrocyte, 36-39, 44, 45
Chorion, placenta, 216, 217
Chorionic villi, 216, 217
Choroid layer of the eye, 228, 229, 232, 233
Chromaffin reaction, 190
Chromatophore, 232, 233
Chromophile cell of pituitary, 182-185
Chromophobe cell of pituitary, 182-185
Chyle vessel, 19
Ciliary body of eye, 228, 229
— muscle, 228, 229
— processes, 228, 229
— zonule, 228
Circular furrow, 110, 111
Circumvallate papillae, 110, 111
Cochlea, 234, 235
Cohnheim's fields, 60, 61
Coiled arteries, 210-217
Collagenous fibers, 30-35
Collecting tubules, 174-177
Columella (Modiolus), 234, 235
Column, anterior (ventral), 74, 75
— posterior (dorsal), 74, 75
— of Clarke, 76, 77
Cones of the retina, 228, 232, 233

Conjunctiva, ocular, 228, 229
— palpebral, 226, 227
Connective tissue, 30-35
— — adipose, 30-33
— — dense, 32, 33
— — loose, 30-33
Cornea, 228-231
— limbus of, 228, 229
Corona radiata, 14, 15, 204, 205
Corpora cavernosa penis, 200, 201
Corpus albicans, 202, 203
— cavernosum urethrae, 200, 201
— luteum, 206, 207
— spongiosum, 200, 201
Corpuscle, Hassall's, 96, 97
— Malpighian, 174
— Meissner's, 100, 101
— Pacinian, 102-103, 162, 163
— renal, 174, 175
Cortex cortici of the kidney, 172, 173
Corti, organ of, 234, 235
— spiral ganglion of, 234, 235
Cortical labyrinth of the kidney, 172
— sinus, 90, 91
Crypt, tonsillar, 98, 99
Crypts of Lieberkühn, 140-153
Cumulus oöphorus, 204, 205
Cuticle, hair, 102, 103

D

DECIDUAL cells, 216, 217
Demilunes, 118-121
Dendrite (Dendron), 62, 63
Dendron (Dendrite), 62, 63
Dental alveolus, 112, 113
— pulp, 114, 115
— sac, 112, 113
Dentin, 112-115
— tubules, 112-113
Dermal papilla, 100-103
Dermis, 100-103
Descemet's membrane, 230, 231
Dorsal (posterior) median sulcus, 74-77
Duct, alveolar, 168, 169, 171
— bile, 154-157
— cochlear, 234, 235
— intercalary, 116-121
— interlobular, 116-119
— intralobular, 116, 118
— lactiferous, 224, 225
— papillary, 176, 177
— striated, 116-121
Ductus deferens, 196, 197
Duodenal (Brunner's) glands, 138-141
Dura mater, 76-77

E

EAR, inner, 234, 235
Eberth's lines, 60, 61

Goblet cells, 18, 19
— — of large intestine, 146, 147
— — of lung, 168-171
— — of rectum, 152
— — of small intestine, 138-145
Goll's column (Fasciculus gracilis), 74, 75
Granulocyte, 50-57
Granulosa lutein cell, 206, 207
Gray commissure, 74-76
— matter, 74-77
Ground substance of bone, 48, 49, 124
— — of cartilage, 36-39
— — of connective tissue, 34, 35

H

HAIR, 100-103
— bulb, 100-103
— follicle, 100-103
Hassall's corpuscle, 96, 97
Haversian canal, 40-43, 48-49
— systems, 40-43, 48-49
Heart: atrium, mitral valve, ventricle, 86, 87
— pulmonary artery, valve, ventricle, 88, 89
Helicotrema, 234, 235
Hemocytoblast, 50-52
Hemorrhoidal plexus, 152, 153
Hemorrhoids, 152
Henle's layer, 102, 103
— loop, 174-177
Hepatic artery, 154-157
— portal vein, 154-157
Hilus of a lymph node, 90, 91
Histiocytes, 30, 31
Holocrine secretion, 102
Howship's lacuna, 46-49
Huxley's layer, 102, 103
Hypophysis (Pituitary gland), 182, 183

I

ILEUM, 98, 99, 142, 143
Infundibular stalk of the pituitary, 182, 183
Intercalary duct, 116-121
Intercalated disks, 60, 61
Intercellular bridges of skin, 100, 101
Interglobular dentin, 112, 113
Interlobular duct, 116-119
— space (Portal area), 154, 156
Interstitial cell, of testis, 192-195
Intestine, large, 146, 147
— small, 138-145
Intralobular duct, 162, 163
Involution, 202
Iris, 228, 229
Islet of Langerhans, 162, 163

J

JEJUNUM, 142, 143

K

KIDNEY, 172-177
Kiernan's fissure, 154, 155
— space (Portal area), 154, 155
Krause, gland of, 226, 227
Kupffer's cells, 156, 157

L

LABIAL glands, 106, 107
Lacrimal gland, 226, 227
— — accessory, 226, 227
Lacteal, 19, 144, 145
Lactiferous duct, 224, 225
Lacunae, Howship's, 46-49
Lacunae of cartilage, 36-39
Lamellae of bone, 40
— — circumferential, 40, 41
— — inner circumferential, 40, 41
— — interstitial (ground), 40, 41
— — outer circumferential, 40, 41
Lamina fusca (Suprachoroid layer), 232
— hepatic (plate), 154-157
— propria of appendix, 148, 149
— — of bladder, 180, 181
— — of cardia, 128, 129
— — of cervix, 218, 219
— — of ductus deferens, 196, 197
— — of esophagus, 122-127
— — of gallbladder, 160, 161
— — of large intestine, 146, 147
— — of lip, 106, 107
— — of rectum, 150, 151
— — of seminal vesicle, 198, 199
      of small intestine, 140-143
— — of stomach, 130-133
— — of tongue, 108-111
— — of trachea, 166, 167
— — of ureter, 178, 179
— — of uterine tube, 208, 209
— — of uterus, 210-215
— — of vagina, 220, 221
Langerhans, Islet of, 162, 163
Large intestine, 146, 147
Larynx, 164, 165
Lens, 228, 229
— suspensory ligament, 228, 229
Lip, 106, 107
Leukocyte, 50-57
Lieberkühn, crypts (glands), 138–145
Lissauer's tract, 74-77
Liver, Altmann's stain of, 158, 159
— Best's carmine stain of, 158, 159
— del Rio Hortega's stain of, 158, 159

Osteocyte, 40, 48-49
Ovarian follicle, 14, 15, 202-205
Ovary, 202-207
Oviduct (Fallopian tube), 208, 209
Oxyphilic cell (Acidophilic cell) of the parathyroids, 188, 189

P

PACINIAN corpuscle in dermis, 101, 102
— — in pancreas, 162, 163
Pancreas, 162-163
— Gomori's stain of, 162-163
Paneth cells, 142, 143
Papilla, circumvallate, 110, 111
— filiform, 108, 109
— fungiform, 108, 109
— of kidney, 172, 173, 176, 177
— optic, 228, 229
Papillary ducts, 176, 177
Parasympathetic ganglion, 130, 131, 140-143, 147-151
Parathyroid glands, 188, 189
Parietal cells of stomach, 132-135
Parotid gland, 116, 117
Pars distalis of pituitary, 182-185
— intermedia of pituitary, 182, 183
— nervosa of pituitary, 182, 183
— tuberalis of pituitary, 182, 183
Pectinate line of rectum, 150, 151
Penis, 200, 201
Perichondrium, 36-39, 44-47
Perimysium, 60, 61
Perineurium, 68-73
Perinodular sinus of lymph node, 92, 93
Periosteum, 44-47
Peritoneum, 147
Peyer's Patch, 98, 99
Pia mater, 74-77
Pilomotor muscle, 101-103
Pituitary gland (Hypophysis), 182-185
— — azan stain of, 184, 185
Placenta, 216, 217
Platelet, blood, 52-57
Polymorphous cell of cerebral cortex, 80, 81
Portal area of the liver, 154-157
Portal vein, 82, 83
Posterior chamber of eye, 228, 229
Posterior (dorsal) median sulcus, 74-77
Postero-intermediate septum, 74-77
Postero-lateral column of spinal cord, 74, 75
Postero-medial column of spinal cord, 74, 75
Predentin, 114, 115
Principal cell (Chief cell) of the parathyroids, 188, 189
— — (Chromophobe cell) of the pituitary, 182-185

Prostate gland, 198, 199
Pulmonary artery, heart, 88, 89
— of lung, 168-171
Pulp cavity, tooth, 112, 113
Purkinje cell of cerebellum, 78, 79
— fibers, of heart, 86, 89
Pyloric glands of stomach, 136-139
Pyloric sphincter, 138, 139
Pyloro-duodenal junction, 138, 139
Pyramid of Malpighi, 172
— of Ferrein, 172
Pyramidal cell of cerebral cortex, 80, 81

R

RANVIER, nodes of, 68-71
Rectal columns, 150
Rectum, 150, 151
Red line of lip, 106, 107
Red pulp, 94, 95
Reissner's (Vestibular) membrane, 234, 235
Remak's fibers, 84
Renal (Malpighian) corpuscle, 174
— papilla, 172, 173, 176, 177
— pyramid, 172
Reticular cell, primitive, 50-53
— fibers in liver, 158, 159
Reticuloendothelium of liver, 156, 157
— of pituitary, 182, 183
Retina, 228, 229, 232, 233
—, blind, 228
—, ciliary, 228, 229
—, iridial, 228
—, optic, 228, 229
Retzius, lines of, 112, 113
Riolan, ciliary muscle of, 228, 229
Rods of retina, 228, 232, 233
Root canal, 112, 113

S

SALIVARY glands, 116-121
Sarcolemma, 58
Sarcoplasm, 58
Scala tympani, 234, 235
— vestibuli, 234, 235
Schmidt-Lantermann clefts, 68, 69
Schreger, bands of, 112, 113
Schwann's sheath (Neurolemma), 70-73
Sclera, 228, 229, 232, 233
Sebaceous gland, 102, 103, 106, 107
— — of penis, 200, 201
Seminal vesicle, 198, 199
Seminiferous tubule, 192-195
Septum, posterior median, 74-77
Serosa of gallbladder, 160, 161
— of large intestine, 146, 147
— of small intestine, 140-143
— of stomach, 130, 131